INSTITUTIONAL NEUROSIS

Gait and posture in institutional neurosis

INSTITUTIONAL NEUROSIS

RUSSELL BARTON

M.B., B.S., F.R.C.P.(C), M.R.C.P.(London), D.P.M.(London),
F.A.C.P., F.R.C.Psych., Diplomate, American Board of
Neurology and Psychiatry (P).

*Director, Rochester Psychiatric Center, New York; Clinical Professor, New York
School of Psychiatry; Associate Clinical Professor of Psychiatry, University of
Rochester School of Medicine and Dentistry; Senior Associate Psychiatrist,
Strong Memorial Hospital, Rochester, New York. Formerly Senior Hospital Medical
Officer, Shenley Hospital; Physician Superintendent, Severalls Hospital, Essex.*

With a Foreword by
NOEL GORDON HARRIS, M.D., F.R.C.P., D.P.M.
*Late Physician for Psychological Medicine, The Middlesex Hospital and Lecturer on
Psychological Medicine, The Middlesex Hospital Medical School.*

THIRD EDITION

JOHN WRIGHT & SONS LTD   BRISTOL 1976

First edition, 1959
Reprinted, 1960
Second edition, 1966
Reprinted, 1970
Third edition, 1976
Reprinted, 1982

Greek edition, 1961
French edition, 1969
Spanish edition, 1974
German edition, 1974

ISBN 0 7236 0388 X

Printed in Great Britain by John Wright & Sons (Printing) Ltd., at The Stonebridge Press, Bristol

Preface to the Third Edition

Since first writing *Institutional Neurosis*, I have reluctantly become aware that to the list of constituent factors collected some twenty years ago must be added violence, brutality, browbeating, harshness, teasing and tormenting. These loathsome practices, carried out unofficially and secretly by a small minority of callous unenlightened staff, are probably an important factor subjugating certain patients into an apathetic, cowed, mute and timorous state. I am amazed and humiliated that with all the evidence given one by patients, ex-patients, relatives and staff I did not identify and record it years ago. It is not a sole cause, however, and Thomas Mann based his description of institutional neurosis in his novel *The Magic Mountain* on sanatoria for patients with pulmonary tuberculosis, where there was no violence yet apathy and dependence developed.

Disclosures of violence in mental hospitals can do harm. They may add yet a further increment of distress to people who need institutional care and to their families. They may blind unthinking members of the public to the enormous kindness, sympathy, forbearance and first class attention that goes on twenty-four hours a day, year in and year out, unwitnessed and unsung. They fuel campaigns to do away with institutions, often mounted with good intentions such as to pressure provision of community services, but sometimes blatant attempts by aspirant entrepreneurs to obtain their property and income without realistically replacing the services they would abolish.

An institution, given adequate funds, staff and executive authority, can be run economically with compassion and clinical competence and provide a psychiatric service to mentally ill in-patients and those in the community. Integration of day care with in-patient care can be successful and facilities such as sheltered workshops, household management units, art studios and so forth can be extended to all who need them. Setting up a duplicate, separately administered, system of community services is expensive in money and manpower. It is much cheaper to staff one two-thousand-bedded hospital than a hundred twenty-bedded units, but the problems of middle management, bureaucracy and the maintenance of employee morale and humane personal programmes become proportionately more difficult as hospitals increase in size. Nevertheless it can be done and institutional neurosis can be eliminated if the principles outlined in this booklet are observed.

My thanks are due to Messrs. John Wright & Sons, of Bristol, the publishers, for their unfailing help and courtesy, and to my wife, Grizel, who typed the manuscript.

1600, South Avenue,   Russell Barton
Rochester, New York.   April 21, 1976

Preface to the Second Edition

During seven years which have elapsed since writing *Institutional Neurosis* I have had opportunities to study mental hospitals in America, China, Europe, and Malta. Nothing has contradicted the initial formulation that apathy, loss of interest, lack of initiative, and sometimes a characteristic posture and gait result from institutional life and is, so to speak, a mental bed-sore.

It has been objected that apathy, withdrawal, impaired judgement about complicated situations, and lack of initiative are found in schizophrenic patients prior to admission to hospital. Since these are the principal features of institutional neurosis, the latter does not merit clinical identity separate from schizophrenia. This objection was dealt with in the first edition. The situation is illustrated by breathlessness in general medicine when a patient with congestive cardiac failure has bronchospasm. Both conditions give rise to breathlessness. It would be foolish to treat only the bronchospasm, or to neglect it while vigorously treating the heart failure. Schizophrenia, depression, mental subnormality, or organic dementia may predispose to withdrawal and apathy, but isolating a patient and forcing him to lead a dependent regimented life will produce apathy and dependence in its own right. The concept, or construct, 'institutional neurosis' has its halo of uncertainty—its penumbra of doubt—as has every other concept or construct in psychiatry. Yet it is a pragmatic concept, vital for assistant nurses, psychiatric technicians, and the great host of untrained or semi-trained but devoted people who mostly care for psychiatric patients around the world.

It can be argued that the effects of institutionalization are not always harmful, and that the aggressive non-conformist criminal may be adequately cowed and sufficiently domesticated to take his place in society by judicious and intelligent institutionalization. This may be so for some antisocial personalities, but certainly not all.

During the last few years systematic investigations of the effect of environment on patients and of illness on patients have been carried out by John Wing and his co-workers of the Medical Research Unit at Maudsley Hospital. Erving Goffman's brilliant work, of which I was unaware when writing the first edition, has appeared as a paperback book *Asylums* and an erudite, but too polysyllabic book

vii

for ordinary mortals, *Ego and Milieu* has been produced by John and Elaine Cumming in the U.S.A. In Minnesota David Vail has produced the concept of dehumanization, and in Vermont George W. Brooks and others have written *The Vermont Story*.

Remotivation therapy, which aims to remotivate patients to take a renewed interest in their surroundings, was developed by the late Dorothy Hoskins Smith, a California teacher and mental hospital volunteer. Now taken over and organized by the mental hospital service of the American Psychiatric Association, it is making an enormous, albeit somewhat stylized, contribution to the care of chronic mentally ill patients in State Hospitals in North America.

As I stated in the first edition, I claim no originality for the ideas presented, I have collected other people's conclusions and then strung them together like beads on a necklace; *Institutional Neurosis* gives an overall picture in simple language and, as before, the references remain the most valuable part of the book.

I wish to record my thanks to my secretary, Miss Myrtle Percival, for her help in preparing the second edition.

Russell Barton
January 1966

Preface to the First Edition

The purpose of this booklet is to present in a systematic form the dreadful mental changes that may result from institutional life and the steps that can be taken to cure them.

I would like to have had opportunity for a more complete study of this man-made disease, observing the similarities and differences in prisons, displaced persons camps, orphanages, convents, and other institutions in different parts of the world. I have confined attention to the material readily available to me in mental hospitals where, unfortunately, there has been a tendency to assume that such mental changes are an end result of mental illness. This is not so. Institutional Neurosis is like a bed-sore. It results from factors other than the illness bringing the patient into hospital. It is, so to speak, 'a mental bed-sore'.

My acknowledgements and thanks are due to Dr Richard Asher who has encouraged me and made many helpful criticisms both literary and technical; to Dr Desmond Bardon who read and annotated the first draft; and to Dr Bernard Gilsenan, who supported various attempts to validate the usefulness of the various methods advocated on his Division at Shenley Hospital, and to Sister Michelle Mauchien who put these into action. It was not possible to carry out a scientific study and although the results are most convincing I have omitted them, not wishing to confuse exposition with validation. I am indebted to Miss H. M. Collins, M.A.O.T., who took all the photographs, and to Mr W. G. Twomey who developed and enlarged them. Also to Miss Constance Orpwood who has typed and re-typed the manuscript.

Finally, I owe a great deal to various members of the staffs of Claybury, Netherne, Warlingham Park, Fulbourne, Hellingly, Banstead, Goodmayes, and Shenley Hospitals, and to others too numerous to mention who have added to, corrected, and clarified my ideas in discussions at various visits and meetings.

Shenley Hospital,   Russell Barton
St. Albans   January 1959

'As Oblomov grew older he reverted to a kind of childish timidity, expecting harm and danger from everything that was beyond the range of everyday life—the result of losing touch with external events.'

I. A. GONCHAROV

Contents

Foreword xiii

1 Consideration, Clinical Features and Differential Diagnosis
of Institutional Neurosis 1

2 Aetiology or Factors associated with Institutional Neurosis 6

3 Consideration of the Factors associated with Institutional
Neurosis 8
 1 *Loss of contact with the outside world*
 2 *Enforced idleness*
 3 *Brutality, browbeating and teasing*
 4 *Bossiness of staff*
 5 *Loss of personal friends, possessions and personal events*
 6 *Drugs*
 7 *Ward atmosphere*
 8 *Loss of prospects outside the institution*

4 Treatment of Institutional Neurosis 22
 1 *Re-establishment of patients' contacts*
 2 *Provision of daily sequence of useful occupations, recreations and
social events* 14 *hours a day,* 7 *days a week*
 3 *Eradication of brutality, browbeating and teasing*
 4 *Alteration of the attitude of professional staff*
 5 *Encourage and make it possible for a patient to have friends,
possessions and to enjoy personal events*
 6 *Reduction of drugs*
 7 *Provision of a homely, friendly, permissive ward atmosphere*
 8 *Make the patient aware of prospects of accommodation, work and
friends outside hospital*

5 Wider Implications of Institutional Neurosis 74

Summary 76

References 78

Index 81

Foreword to the First Edition

This is a book that should have been written many years ago and Dr Russell Barton is to be congratulated on writing it now. It must have needed considerable moral courage on his part to do so.

I suppose that the majority of people have at some time or other in their lives cogitated on loneliness and the unhappiness that it can bring. Few have experienced the enforced loneliness of being cut off from normal human contact through, say, imprisonment, solitary confinement, the concentration camp, or the type of illness which necessitates segregation from one's fellow human creatures and ordinary life.

When I first started to specialize in mental illness in 1923—not really so very long ago—I went to a County Mental Hospital as an Assistant Medical Officer. I was very recently qualified and yet I was put in charge of the male side consisting of the admission ward, the infirmary wards, and the 'chronic' wards. In all I was responsible for about five hundred patients as well as other work.

The female side, which contained about eight hundred patients, was looked after by two more senior medical officers. The Medical Superintendent simply did the administrative work and really no clinical work.

I still remember the rows of patients so often sitting doing nothing; especially I recall the 'airing courts', which I do not think Dr Russell Barton mentions, in which all the year round for an hour or two every morning and afternoon except in very bad weather the patients had to walk round and round on asphalt surrounded in the older courts by high stone walls. Another constant feature was the routine 'ladling' out of sedatives. Yet, the hospital I was at was considered one of the better and more progressive ones.

It was possible to demonstrate, however, that many of the nurses with teaching and enthusiasm were soon able to alter their attitude to patients and that sedatives could be cut down tremendously and prescribed for individual patients.

Dr Russell Barton has described admirably in his book how with modern progress in some forms of treatment and more knowledge of rehabilitation the patients can be helped infinitely more if only the whole attitude of those who care for the mentally ill be altered towards establishing individual support and friendship.

xiii

I think that Dr Russell Barton has perhaps let off too lightly those of us who have specialized in Psychological Medicine and worked in Mental Hospitals. After all, it is the medical man who should take the initiative and arouse enthusiasm in those who work with him, and I fear that in the past and even at the present time this has sometimes been lacking.

I hope that the appropriate Authorities and members of the Press will read this book. How can this work be carried out without adequate finance and a sufficient number of staff; how much more difficult it is to be progressive and to take justifiable risks if on the rare occasion when something goes wrong the Press publishes glaring headlines and often a most misleading account of the incident.

I do not like the title of this book very much, but it is hard to choose a more suitable one and the author has explained why he chose this particular title.

In the future there should be many people grateful to Dr Russell Barton for writing this book.

November 1959   Noel Gordon Harris

Chapter 1

Consideration, Clinical Features and Differential Diagnosis of Institutional Neurosis

Myerson (1939) claimed that the usual hospital care given to schizophrenic patients produced a 'Prison Stupor' or 'Prison Psychosis' which interacted with the social retreat of the original schizophrenia. The patient was put into a motivational vacuum.

Bettelheim and Sylvester (1948) used 'Psychological Institutionalism' to describe the detachment isolation, automaton-like rigidity, passive adjustment and general impoverishment of personality which they noted in emotionally disturbed children in an institution. They remarked: 'Behaviour disorders in the common sense do not necessarily form part of this clinical picture.'

Martin (1955) used the term 'institutionalization' to denote the syndrome of submissiveness, apathy and loss of individuality that is encountered in many patients who have been some time in a mental hospital.

In 1956 I began using the term 'institutional neurosis' in various handouts to the nursing staff with whom I developed programmes of rehabilitation at Shenley Hospital.

Wing (1962) referred to the condition as 'Institutionalism' and Gruenberg (1962) introduced the term 'social breakdown syndrome'. Vail (1966) discussed it under the title 'Dehumanization' and Wallace (1967) refers to 'the syndrome of hospitalism' to describe a patient's loss of his outside identity as spouse, parent, worker or citizen for a new identity—that of a good, passive, chronic patient. It seems that the condition will continue to be discovered and renamed every few years.

I prefer the term 'institutional neurosis' because it promotes the syndrome to the category of a disease, rather than a process, thereby encouraging us to understand, approach and deal with it in the same way as other diseases.

The adjective 'institutional' does not imply that institutions are the only cause of the disorder, but signifies only that institutions are the places where it was first generally recognized, as the use of 'Bornholm' in Bornholm's* disease. By no means all people in institutions develop it, and probably hermits, some housewives and old age pensioners are afflicted with similar symptoms although living alone. 'Oblomovism', so often seen, and brilliantly depicted by Goncharov (1858), is probably a kindred disorder, an indolence and lethargy resulting from conditions in the environment in which the patient lives.

The term 'neurosis' is used rather than 'psychosis', since the syndrome itself does not interfere with the patient's ability to distinguish between reality and fantasy. Indeed such passivity adjusts the individual to the demands of reality in the institution but, at the same time, it hampers or may prevent his return and adjustment to the world outside. 'Neurosis' is used in a general descriptive sense. It describes symptoms and signs, not psychodynamic hypotheses.

The purpose of this monograph is to describe the clinical features of the disorder in mental hospitals, its differential diagnosis, aetiology, treatment and prevention.

I feel sure that the term 'institutional neurosis' has been used already by workers in hospitals in this and other countries who recognize the condition. Furthermore, I claim no originality for most of the ideas presented; my purpose is to try to arrange them in an orderly manner so that they are more easily understood, more readily accepted, and more systematically treated.

Clinical Features

Institutional neurosis is a disease characterized by apathy, lack of initiative, loss of interest more marked in things and events not immediately personal or present, submissiveness, and sometimes no expression of feelings of resentment at harsh or unfair orders. There is also lack of interest in the future and an apparent inability to make practical plans for it, a deterioration in personal habits, toilet and standards generally, a loss of individuality, and a resigned

---

* Bornholm is a Danish island in the Baltic Sea. In 1933 a Danish physician, Sylvest, described an outbreak there of epidemic pleurodynia, a virus infection of the pleura characterized by severe chest pain—which one patient described as the Devil's grip—fever and headache. Although the illness had been recognized and described in Germany, Norway, Iceland and the U.S.A. during the preceding 200 years the name 'Bornholm' has been applied since Sylvest's monograph appeared—but of course the disease occurs all over the world.

acceptance that things will go on as they are—unchangingly, inevitably and indefinitely.

These signs vary in severity from the mute stuporose patient who sits in the same chair day after day, through the ward worker who has without protest surrendered the rest of her existence to the institution, to the active cheerful patient who enjoys the facilities available, often does some handicraft during the day, but shows no desire to leave the hospital, shows no interest in plans for a future in the world outside, and raises numerous difficulties and objections when anyone tries to help her to be discharged.

Occasionally the passive, submissive cooperation of the patient is punctuated by aggressive episodes which are casually attributed to mental illness but which, if carefully investigated, often seem to be provoked by some unkindness from another patient, a hospital employee or visitors. At other times an apparently similar provocation may produce no such response.

The patient often adopts a characteristic posture (*Frontispiece*), the hands held across the body or tucked behind an apron, the shoulders drooped and the head held forward. The gait has a shuffling quality, movements at the pelvis, hips and knees are restricted, although physical examination shows a full range of movement at these joints. The muscular power is found to be good when the patient cooperates in testing it. It may be that this posture develops through prolonged sitting and too little exercise. It was evident in chronic populations of hospitals and workhouses long before the introduction of phenothiazines in 1953, drugs which produce a somewhat similar posture known as Parkinsonism.

New patients arriving at the hospital may notice this posture. One patient in hospital for two months said: 'I'm terrified of being sent where the women walk about with their hands under their aprons with no sign of life in them.'

Further evidence that an institutional neurosis is present may be found in patients' notes (Martin, 1955). A severe neurosis will often have resulted in entries such as: 'Dull, depressed and solitary', or 'Simple, mute and dirty', or 'Dull, apathetic and childish', or 'Remains uncommunicative, withdrawn and unoccupied', or 'Sits about all day and is quite lost'.

And in a mild example of the syndrome may be found remarks such as: 'Unoccupied and lacking in initiative', or 'Works well but has no spontaneity', or 'Has settled down well', or 'Is cooperative and gives no trouble'.

Permutations of these words and phrases, 'institutionalized', 'dull', 'apathetic', 'withdrawn', 'inaccessible', 'solitary', 'unoccupied', 'lacking in initiative', 'lacking in spontaneity', 'uncommunicative', 'simple', 'childish', 'gives no trouble', 'has settled down well', 'is

3

cooperative', should always make one suspect that the process of institutionalization has produced a neurosis. Such remarks were often found in the notes of chronic patients who had been in hospital for many years but who were sufficiently improved after one year's treatment to leave hospital and lead an independent life outside and others who were considerably improved but remained in hospital. When reviewing such a case one must persistently ask oneself to what extent and to whom do such remarks apply. To the patient? To medical staff? To nurses? To attendants? To administrators? To those ultimately responsible for the psychiatric service?

Differential Diagnosis

Only in the past few years has it been recognized that the symptoms described above indicate a disorder separate from the one first responsible for bringing the patient into hospital, and that the disease is produced by methods of looking after people in mental hospitals and is not part of the mental illness preceding and sometimes existing with it.

The condition may be indistinguishable from the later stages of schizophrenia. Often it is complicated by residual schizophrenic features such as delusions or hallucinations. In such cases the diagnosis can only be made retrospectively after subjecting the patient to an intensive course of rehabilitation.

Depressive illnesses have many features in common with institutional neurosis, but the gloominess, sadness, guilt, agitation and despondency of depression are absent in institutional neurosis.

Organic dementias, such as arrested general paralysis of the insane and those of arteriopathic and allegedly arteriopathic origin, are easy to diagnose when neurological signs are present, but it may be difficult to realize that a supervening institutional neurosis is complicating and sometimes largely responsible for the mental picture. Again the only way to decide is retrospectively; to try an intensive rehabilitation programme directed at re-establishing the work habit on one hand and resocialization on the other.

Myxoedema may be distinguished by the typical face, croaking voice, constipation, and raised serum cholesterol, SGOT, LDH and CPK with lowered serum thyroxine, T_3, P.B.I., radioactive iodine uptake and so forth. The tendency to bury oneself under the bed-clothes is common to both conditions.

It may be argued that the fact that treatment causes the disappearance of some of the symptoms ascribed to institutional neurosis is insufficient evidence to justify formulating a disease entity. However, other supporting evidence is that a similar set of symptoms is sometimes found in people without mental disorders in other institutions—prisoner-of-war camps, displaced persons camps,

4

orphanages, tuberculosis sanatoria, prisons and convents. The symptoms are also encountered as an end result of many different disorders and, as Martin remarks, 'It can hardly be argued that mental illness in general, regardless of its type produces an end state similar to institutionalization'. Asher (1947) described the effect of prolonged bed rest on some patients with physical, not psychiatric disorders: 'At a later stage a dismal lethargy overcomes the victim. . . . The end result can be a comatose vegetable existence in which, like a useless but carefully tended plant, the patient lies permanently in tranquil torpidity.'

Chapter 2

Aetiology or Factors associated with Institutional Neurosis

The cause of institutional neurosis is uncertain. It does not seem to have a single cause. It is associated with many factors in the environment in which the patient lives. Possibly the patients react with a tendency common to most human beings to modify ambition and establish a way of life as trouble-free and secure as possible.

Though with a little ingenuity the end result might be explained in terms of conditioning, psychoanalysis, or analytical psychology, I believe the outline in general descriptive terms already given, followed by a systematic description of the factors present in the associated environment of the institution, is more valuable. As Sydenham remarked: 'In writing a natural history of diseases, every merely philosophical hypothesis should be set aside, and the manifest and natural phenomena, however minute, should be noted with the utmost exactness.' One must not confuse association with causation. It is always important to look for facts and not merely confirmation of one's hypotheses.

The idea (or construct) of the illness, institutional neurosis, has largely been obtained from reports of successful treatment by various authors. I hope that setting out these discoveries in an orderly fashion will help in recognizing and treating the disorder.

The factors commonly found in the environment can be grouped conveniently under eight headings. Of course, the divisions are not absolute and these factors overlap one another.

The eight factors are:
1. Loss of contact with the outside world.
2. Enforced idleness.
3. Brutality, browbeating and teasing.
4. Bossiness of staff.
5. Loss of personal friends, possessions and personal events.

6. Drugs.
7. Ward atmosphere.
8. Loss of prospects outside the institution.

I would stress that these eight groups are clusters of factors each as different from the others as possible. They are artificial divisions of an overall picture.

Examination of these groups of factors reveals some overlap. Although experience may give the impression that correction of a single factor will in some cases bring about the dramatic recovery, i.e. discovery of a relative who begins to make regular visits, reflection makes one realize that it is difficult, if not impossible, for one factor to alter without others.

Scrutiny of each of these constituent factors separately enables us to get a better understanding of the total process of institutionalization of which they are part.

Since writing the first edition of *Institutional Neurosis* I have reluctantly become aware that to the list of constituent factors collected some twenty years ago must be added violence, brutality, bullying, browbeating, harshness, teasing and tormenting. These loathsome practices are far more common in institutions than we realized in the 1950's. They are considered as factor number 3 in this third edition and, combined, are probably the most powerful single factor acting to subjugate patients into an apathetic, cowed, mute and timorous state. I am amazed and humiliated that with all the evidence given me by patients, relatives and staff—especially those I was treating—I did not identify and record it years ago.

Chapter 3

Consideration of the Factors associated with Institutional Neurosis

1. Loss of Contact with the Outside World

Locked doors; parole

The patient's loss of contact with the outside world begins with his illness. The process is increased by removal to a mental hospital, often some miles from his home, and maintained by detention behind locked doors, systems of parole, and begrudged or condescending granting of leave often made more difficult by complicated form-filling rituals.

Difficulty in getting leave

Wording of the leave form reads something like this: 'Leave has been granted to . . . on the understanding that . . .'

Little encouragement to relatives to write to patient

Relations write to patients, but very rarely do nurses, doctors, attendants or welfare staff write back to say how much letters are appreciated.

Difficulties for patient to write home

Patients may write to relations if they can get pen, ink and a quiet place to write at the same time. This is difficult in many wards. Only the exceptional superior shows her nurses and attendants how to encourage patients to write home regularly.

Poor facilities for visitors

Visiting is often limited to two hours twice a week, often at times when relations are working. To visit at other times is often regarded

8

as a favour bestowed by staff. The number of visitors is sometimes limited; provision for their welcome and entertainment in the ward may be poor.

Authorities need to make plans now to provide wards, villas, day hospitals and out-patient clinics, with adequate car-parking space for the potential increase of cars in the future. It is becoming almost as important that a hospital should provide adequate parking for visitors as that it should be reasonably near patients' homes.

Distance and time to visit; expense of visiting

The hospital may be many miles from the place the patient came from, difficult to get to by virtue of crowding on buses on visiting days, and expense—the cost of a return journey for two visitors— may be considerable. An afternoon off work may result in loss of pay. Freudenberg et al. (1957) have shown that the closer a patient's relations live to the mental hospital the more likely is he to be discharged. Brown (1959) has produced evidence to show that there is a large positive relationship between a stay of two years in hospital and a failure to receive visitors in the first two months' stay.

Buses and travelling; patients' appearance may repulse laymen

Patients may have forgotten how to get on a bus, how to use money, ask the way, or how to dress so that they will not offend people they meet.

Thus the patient's abnormal responses to the features and events in his life 'occasioned' by illness may be augmented by the unfamiliar and abnormal features and events confronting him in the mental hospital.

In the past many patients never again got the chance to react to a normal environment.

2. Enforced Idleness

It is difficult to convey the idea of *how* patients are forced to be idle. It may be that the principle that rest assists Nature to cure has been drummed into doctors and nurses in their training and uncritically applied to mental disorders. The training received by doctors and nurses in general hospitals has tended to make them run mental hospitals on similar lines. Possibly the neat teaching hospital ward with bed trays at the foot of the bed shown in the *Hurt Mind* T.V. series in 1956 will be as incomprehensible to the doctor of 100 years hence as the picture of pus-stiffened operating aprons of 100 years ago is to us.

If the patients' day is followed from awakening onwards it may give some idea as to how idleness is thrust upon them.

Attendants prevent patients from making beds, etc.

In many wards, attendants, perhaps assisted by one or two special patients, make beds for the patients, and if asked why, reply 'It is quicker to do it yourself,' or 'Many don't make them properly,' or 'It takes them so long to get going.' Many patients may not be allowed to wash or bath themselves: such overcautious nursing has long been enforced in many mental hospitals to the patients' detriment. After getting dressed, often with help, patients may wait idly for their turn in the communal wash-house, because of failure to organize groups with alternative activity. This is followed by a further period of sitting at table while nursing assistants, attendants and a few ward workers bring round meals.

After breakfast patients may be herded into the day room or garden and left to sit. A few may indulge in desultory occupational therapy such as knitting or rug making. If a patient gets up she may be told to sit down; if she asks to go out she may be snubbed or kept waiting. Individual activity of almost any sort may make the nurse afraid of imminent aggression. The nurse's behaviour may actually cause an aggressive act which may then be countered by sedation. Towards the end of the morning it is lunch time; the patient has no hand in purchasing, choosing or preparing the raw materials or serving the finished product.

After lunch a few patients may help clear away or a queue may file past a table putting dirty crockery and cutlery on it. The regular ward workers then set to and wash up, supervised by a nurse or ward orderly.

The afternoon often presents another arid vista of idleness— nothing to do, no one to talk to, nowhere to go, the only event to look forward to being tea and, later, a sedative and bed.

In some wards tea may be laid and prepared as early as 3.0 p.m., the bread placed on the table already buttered, and nurses may spread jam on it. Preparations for bed may start as soon as tea has finished at 4.0 p.m., and often patients are in bed by 6.0 p.m.

3. Brutality, Browbeating and Teasing

In most institutions a minority of unenlightened staff secretly physically assault patients who are not compliant—perhaps regarding them as disobedient children and meting out corrective measures maybe once applied to themselves and which they apply to their own children.

Brutality, browbeating, rough handling, harshness, teasing and general ill-treatment always lie latent in institutions, smouldering and ready to burst into flames at any time. Management must make the presumption that it will occur even if staff are adequately inspired, motivated, supervised and investigated whenever doubt arises. The presumption that such things do not or cannot happen has been shown again and again to be naïve and fatuous. There are always a few brutes and bullies among a staff of any size and in the small hours of the morning and at other times when there is nobody about they have a free hand. Senior administrators, office psychiatrists and nurses, members of hospital management committees, regional authorities and State departmental or Governmental officers and many members of the public simply cannot believe that brutality and harshness are possible. Maybe they find the prospect of bullying mentally ill and defenceless people so repugnant they cannot accept that anyone would do such a thing. Usually management and administrative officers feel hurt and let down by witnesses who draw attention to such matters, and fail to make adequate investigations. When their hand is forced by public outcry to look into the matter impartially, they become more critical and resentful of whoever makes the complaint. Most shameful is the retribution which sometimes follows when an inquiry reveals brutality. The witnesses reporting incidents leading to the investigation are often victimized by management and ostracized by fellow employees. *Ad hominem* arguments are levelled against them; they are said to be 'trouble makers' or 'settling old scores' or 'seeking the limelight'. Undoubtedly at times the motivation for drawing the attention of the authorities to brutality is malicious and a result of personal animosities. But in many instances it should be regarded as a very courageous gesture by a poorly paid attendant or nurse who stands to gain nothing and who risks her livelihood by coming forward.

I do not expect my assertions to be taken as the fact of these matters. Unacceptable as they may be, the facts can be found in the published reports of various inquiries into the ill-treatment of mentally ill people which have appeared with monotonous regularity over the past two hundred years. Some of these are mentioned in Kathleen Jones's book *History of the Mental Health Services* (1972); others have been the subject of sensational reporting in newspapers in Britain and the United States. The pity is that these lessons have to be learned over and over by direct experience to the detriment and misery and terror of patients. The most recent and maybe most closely scrutinized evidence comes from a series of reports starting in 1967 with Barbara Robb's book *Sans Everything*, an account of brutality, harshness and ill-treatment in various institutions in England. Sensationalized reporting of this book caused a public furor. Inquiries were set up into each incident but witnesses were not privileged nor legally aided, so that their evidence was given under the threat of a libel action; and due process, the time-honoured and most civilized method of arriving at truth and the keystone of our system of justice, failed to produce admissible evidence. The

Government 'Report on the Enquiries into *Sans Everything*' (1968) (Cmnd. 3687) caused C. H. Rolfe to epigram public scepticism in the title of his article in the *New Statesman*—'Whitehall Washes Whiter'.

A breakthrough occurred in 1969 when a committee chaired by Mr (now Sir) Geoffrey Howe, Q.C., carried out an inquiry into allegations made to the *News of the World* about the ill-treatment of patients and pilfering by members of the staff at Ely Hospital, Cowbridge Road, Cardiff. The committee's report (Cmnd. 3975) left the public in no doubt that brutality, ill-treatment, undue roughness and teasing had occurred.

Subsequently, further reports on different hospitals appeared: Farleigh (1971) (Cmnd. 4557), Whittingham (1972) (Cmnd. 4861)* and South Ockendon (1974) established beyond reasonable doubt that brutality occurs and should always be watched for and investigated. Since they have been named these hospitals have borne the brunt of public odium and contempt, the public being heedless of all good work they have done. There but for the grace of God go many other hospitals, for very few of these practices are reported and when they are, the investigation flounders and publicity is successfully avoided.

Haematoma auris, 'the insane ear', well known to asylum doctors and reported by writers 100 years ago, was almost certainly traumatic and due to an unwritten tradition among certain ignorant,

---

* The Whittingham Hospital Report omits a fact that caused me a great deal of personal distress and embarrassment. In February 1965, following a lecture at the Annual Conference of the National Association for Mental Health in Church House, London, I was challenged to give an example of a hospital where such conditions of ill-treatment could be found. I named Whittingham Hospital. A sensational report appeared in the local press; I received hostile letters from the Chairmen of their Management and Medical Advisory Committees demanding withdrawal and apology. I refused. In November 1965 I was called before the ethical committee of the British Medical Association and subsequently censured. I now value this scar highly among my battle honours. The local press report encouraged Dr A. B. Masters, then an Assistant Psychiatrist at Whittingham Hospital, together with the student nurses to continue to make complaints and representations on behalf of the patients. In 1968 they were joined by Mrs Patricia Bunn who was appointed as Principal Psychologist in March of that year. Their continued efforts to humanize the conditions for patients showed a vocational dedication of the highest order and an unusual courage and persistency. I salute them.

Their campaign resulted in the committee of inquiry and public investigations, a male nurse was charged with murder and causing grievous bodily harm to a patient and convicted of manslaughter and imprisoned—a tragedy for him but necessary in stamping out brutality.

Dr A. B. Masters, realizing he had jeopardized his prospects in the National Health Service in England, emigrated to Canada, became disenchanted with the Government Service there, and is now in private practice in Regina, Saskatchewan.

callous attendants that brutality was necessary and justifiable in managing mentally ill people. Just as the ears of animals are gripped and twisted to move them from stall to stall at market, so were patients treated. Malnutrition probably worsened the effects of trauma and together with murder accounted for the high mortality of this condition.

Brutality is unsanctioned and usually goes undetected through the misplaced loyalty of other staff (only a traitorous deviant would turn in a fellow employee), and the intimidation of witnesses. It is usually unsuspected, usually denied and in many cases covered up by hospital authorities (since they themselves are held responsible) and thus it is condoned and perpetuated.

The usual brutality is slapping a patient's head or face, punching or assaulting with a stick or a wet towel.

Other forms of physical assault are beating patients in a boot room or bathroom with a rubber-soled slipper, punching in the abdomen with a wet towel round the fist, tossing in a blanket, twisting a wet towel round the neck, shaking and shoving so that the victim falls or hits his head against a wall. A ruthless attendant can encourage patients to beat up a patient who is causing trouble.

Rough handling of patients is a form of brutality in which physical coercion is used without actual hitting. Examples are: frog marching, dragging, gripping by the arms, shoving, pushing and forcing into chairs, into showers, on to a bed and so forth. Rough handling merges with brutality, on the one hand, and with that minimal and reluctantly applied physical force occasionally necessary for a few patients, on the other. In some institutions force is never necessary —they do not dispense with it by being more humane as their spokesmen sometimes pretend, but by refusing to admit difficult patients or giving them large doses of tranquillizers. Any psychiatric service providing care for the complete range of mentally disordered people will occasionally have to resort to some physical contact. However, there is a world of difference between a guiding hand, a forceful grip and clenched fist.

Harshness

Cruel, unfeeling behaviour, thwarting a patient's wishes, humiliating patients in front of other people, belittling them, deliberately keeping them waiting before unlocking a door, before giving them their meal, before answering their questions or attending to their requests, is harsh and unacceptable treatment. Being hypercritical, unfriendly, lacking an amiable affable attitude creates a distressing, hostile atmosphere of reluctance and resentment which makes another human being feel miserably unimportant or impotently inferior. Telling a patient she is a nuisance, a social parasite, a mental case, a filthy old wet, a dirty girl or scolding her for doing things she cannot help or does not realize, is humiliating to adult people and is not good nursing. Such behaviour makes a patient despair of finding kindliness, friendship and happiness ever again.

Before judging staff too harshly it must be remembered that mentally ill and elderly people can be maddening and exasperating and the chronic shortage of staff in most situations results in all but the most saintly employees becoming irritable and short tempered at times. The self-righteous politician or opportunist crusader should work eight hours a day 'with his hands in excreta' for a few days before exploiting these tragic incidents with harsh criticism, calculated to gain himself public popularity and esteem. Such efforts may result in a dull-witted bully being fired but may not achieve anything else.

Browbeating

Browbeating consists of bullying, threatening, bearing down on a patient by shouting, talking in a loud authoritative voice, not listening to what patients have to say and disregarding their wishes and requests. Sometimes relatives or friends are guilty but too often it is untrained institutional staff who do this to mentally ill people. The combination of badgering, hectoring, harassing, shouting and a stern ill-tempered voice is acutely distressing to most patients who lie doggo, going quiet and passive in an attempt to avoid further provocation and possible violence and to terminate an unpleasant and frightening situation. Constant exposure to such subjugation, I now realize, is probably the most powerful single factor making patients in an institution apathetic, cowed, mute and timorous. Suddenly lifting one's hand will make patients who have been ill-treated involuntarily cringe—this supports but does not prove that browbeating and violence has occurred.

Teasing and tormenting

Making jokes or playful accusations at the expense of a patient, subjecting patients to petty annoyances, kidding them that their spouse has found someone else, that they have lost their leave privileges and so forth constitute a method by which inexperienced, insensitive people attempt to relate to mentally ill people. Most unskilled employees intially have feelings of incompetence toward patients who make them feel inept. The resulting hostility is vented by teasing and tormenting patients. Horseplay is more common when poorly trained or untrained staff are unsupervised than is enerally realized. A jovial frivolous approach is misplaced in the day-to-day relationship between attendant and patient—although humour and fun are invaluable at times. Neither attendant nor patient should act, nor be forced to act, the clown. Tormenting may be a socially acceptable form of attenuated aggression among normal people. It is thoughtlessly cruel to patients whose mental illness makes them dependent on staff.

4. Bossiness of Staff

This is often a firmly established feature encountered when an attempt is made to institute a rehabilitation programme. Most people make an implicit assumption that they are personally superior, more valuable, more worth while than a mentally ill person. Not that every attendant, nurse or doctor is authoritative, nor that every attendant preserves the same attitude all the time she is on duty. It is foolish to stereotype people, but it is very necessary to explore the prevailing attitudes in a mental hospital.

There are probably more kind and friendly employees than otherwise, but it is my impression that an authoritarian attitude is the rule rather than the exception. It is revealed in many ways, e.g. the use of the imperative mood in written orders: 'Patients will not leave the ward', 'Nurses will report immediately . . .'. Orders are often given in a dictatorial voice such as 'Sit down', 'At once', 'When *I* tell you', 'How dare you', 'You know you mustn't . . .', 'I've told you before . . .'. Patients have been shouted at across a ward and grabbed by the arms or clothing and forced into a chair (*see above*, Section 3).

Again this attitude may be revealed by asking a patient questions when an attendant is present. The attendant will chip in with 'Come on, tell the doctor . . .'. It is sometimes impossible to have a minute's silence with a patient if an attendant is present, yet in ordering the patient to comply with the doctor's requests the attendant is trying to help the doctor, thus depriving him of the opportunity to make clinical observations on a patient who is unharassed and at ease.

There is a tendency for attendants to decide which clothes, shoes and aprons a patient must wear, if and when and how their hair is dressed, where they *must* sit at table, which bed they must sleep in at night, what personal possessions they can have, if any, how much pocket money and 'extra comforts' they can appreciate, if and when they can leave the ward, and so on. In some wards three doors had to be unlocked to enable patients to go from the day room to the lavatory. Needless to say, the incidence of incontinence was high.

If questioned, attendants often defend their decisions with 'The patient is too deteriorated to know', or 'The patient is too mad to know what she wants'. Instead of encouraging independence and nurturing initiative with the greatest care, the attendant is taking

15

the patient out of her own life by doing everything and making all decisions for her. The attendant often has had no option but to do so because of the way many mental hospitals have been run. In many cases nobody has ever shown her how to treat patients properly and how to handle them without browbeating them.

It would be too naïve to suppose that when *psychiatric* nursing by nurses and attendants falls below standard the supervising nurses, Head Nurses, Nurse Tutor or Director of Nursing, are to blame. It is invalid to blame any individual, for individuals change frequently but mental hospitals have remained unchanged. Blame lies on the group and each member is guilty to some extent. No useful purpose is served by witch hunting. Henry (1954), Bockoven (1956) and Clark (1958) have suggested that it is a fault of administrative structure. Many workers are responsible to more than one supervisor. A nurse in charge of a ward may receive conflicting instructions from a consultant, a ward doctor, a supervising nurse and an administrator. The greater the number of persons to whom she is responsible, the greater the danger of disagreement, the greater the tension, and the worse the atmosphere. She is only really safe doing the paper work demanded, housekeeping and routine chores, and giving orders as necessary to implement hospital policy. A male nurse gloomily summarized the situation by saying: 'There are too many people with too much authority and too little responsibility; and too many with too much responsibility and too little authority.' Brevity makes the remark attractive but it is an oversimplification, not completely true.

Because authority is likely to be misused it does not mean that anarchy should replace it. In the absence of good government, petty tyrannies and bullying may spring up which may be worse than supervised structural authority, albeit at times misused. Effective executive authority is essential in a hospital or a ward.

In the first two editions of this book my observations were made on the staffing present in the wards at that time—nurses and doctors. Since then I have had the opportunity to observe the introduction of a non-medical body of mental hygiene therapists with a separate career ladder. This introduction has not solved the problem. Non-medical team leaders and staff usually make the assumption of personal superiority and become bossy and dictatorial just as easily and quickly as their predecessors.

5. Loss of Personal Friends, Possessions and Personal Events

Personal friends

Personal friends may visit the patient at first but very soon the combination of expense, difficulty in travelling, and small welcome from the patient on the ward makes the visits less frequent until they eventually cease. There are many people, however, who have visited regularly each week for many years. One woman had got a part-time job in order to make her weekly three-hour journey from Southend, Essex, to the hospital in St Albans and bring the patient little gifts. Another patient had been visited regularly from admission in 1940 all through the war years until 1955. Visiting stopped when a doctor rebuked her relations because they complained that the patient had been moved to another ward.

The possibility of one patient making a friend and confidant of another inside a mental hospital is great, but it is surprising how infrequently it happens. The importance to children of continued contact with one person has been emphasized by Bettelheim and Sylvester (1948). Isolation, lack of purpose and loneliness beget apathy which in turn causes further isolation.

Personal possessions

Large numbers of patients in some mental hospitals have no place in which they can keep personal possessions, no lockers by their bed. Keeping all patients' possessions in a single property room is a bad system. It means in practice the property is hardly ever available for patient use. Often clothes are issued to a ward and there may be no guarantee that if a patient keeps her frock clean one day she will wear the same one the next day. Similarly photographs of her family, writing paper and such essentials as combs, tooth-brushes, cosmetics, etc., are difficult and often impossible to keep. One hospital refused to accept any personal property with patients admitted as late as 1958. Many are still very restrictive. Every patient should be allowed one suitcase and a hold-all. The hospital should have authority to dispose of personal belongings of patients who have left to a lost property office 28 days after they have been notified.

The importance of personal possessions is an everyday experience. A feature observed by the writer when working in Belsen concentration camp at the end of World War II was the importance attached by inmates, who were not too ill or apathetic, to small personal possessions—a diary, a photograph, a tin mug, and so on. In the book *The White Rabbit*, by Bruce Marshall (1952), the personal importance of Hubble's chess set is noted.

Personal events

Personal events such as family birthdays, weddings, children's school holidays, return of children and husband in the evening, getting them off in the morning, weekends with them at home on Saturday afternoon and Sunday, going out to work, visiting friends, the pub, the cinema, bowling or looking forward to a programme on television or wireless in the evening are a few examples of the myriads of more or less pleasurable personal events punctuating the patient's life which she once had to look forward to and could look back on. In the mental hospital she has lost her role. Institutional events exist but the patient plays no part in ordering or altering them; they are largely impersonal. There is little to look forward to, and little to look back on. One day blurs into the next, weeks merge with months and suddenly a lifetime has passed by.

6. Drugs

Sedatives produce apathy.

The main job of medical officers in mental hospitals has been to make daily ward rounds, to sign the medicine cards and document routine physical and mental examinations. Meeting the demands of paper work has always been more important than the needs of patients.

It is not surprising that the majority of patients forced to go to bed by 7.0 p.m. after an idle day require sedatives to sleep, nor that they wake after 8 hours at 3.0 or 4.0 a.m. (or are awakened by the clanking keys and noise caused by the rounds nurse who may shine a torch on them) and then require more sedatives for further sleep. If, as sometimes happens, these be given at 4.0 a.m. the patient may be difficult to awaken at 6.0 a.m. and not in a very fit state to make her bed, complete her toilet and help with breakfast. The effect of the sedative may not wear off for 4–12 hours after it is given, so that during the morning the apathy produced by the absence of a planned routine and loss of contact with the world outside the hospital is furthered by the effects of paraldehyde, barbituric acid derivatives or the more modern tranquillizing drugs, chlorpromazine and reserpine. Just as a whiff of smoke is given to quieten bees so are sedatives and tranquillizers sometimes used to quieten patients.

During the day paraldehyde or barbiturates have been favourite remedies for patients with 'disturbed behaviour'. Others may be having regular sedation with paraldehyde, barbituric acid derivatives, reserpine or phenothiazines, some of which not only predispose to apathy but may also cause addiction which binds the patient to the mental hospital even more strongly and makes the idea of discharge repugnant.

Drugging often starts with the admission ward. The staff may almost routinely ask for the patient to have '6 gr of Sodium Amytal or 2 oz of haustus paraldehyde' or something as a standby if he cannot sleep. Electric convulsive therapy is sometimes repeatedly given to disturbed patients. It quietens them down, often confuses them for several hours, but has no place in the long-term treatment of patients.

7. Ward Atmosphere

By this is meant the general impression a ward creates. Such an impression from a patient's point of view is the sum total of many different factors, such as:

    a. Colour of walls, ceilings, floors, lino and carpets.

    b. Colours and designs of furniture, beds, chairs, windows, lamp-shades, pictures, fireguards, rugs, carpets, cushions, curtains.

    c. Intensity of illumination (brightness).

    d. Space, arrangement of furniture, etc., and presence or absence of crowding.

    e. Views from the windows.

    f. Flies and presence or absence of dirtiness, dinginess and dilapidation.

    g. Appearance of other patients: hair styles, hair on faces, clothes, stockings, shoes. Wearing of aprons in sitting-rooms, etc.

    h. Noise: clatter of ward activity, jangling of keys, television sets playing, doors slamming, telephones ringing, noise of electric cleaners, patients shouting and sounds coming from without.

    i. The friendliness, smartness and helpfulness or the off-handedness, untidiness and unhelpfulness of the charge nurse and attendants to patients, to each other and to relatives. It means a lot to most patients to see their relatives getting on well with the staff.

    j. Smell of the ward: the smell of faeces, vomit, urine, cats, paraldehyde, disinfectant, mothballs, cooking, ozone machines, or the smell of flowers, talc and freshness.

    k. Temperature of the ward, and humidity (sterilizers in a ward can make it very humid), air movement and draughts.

    l. The other patients' reactions to the ward, their relationship with nurses and their attitude to visitors.

    m. Posture, activity and occupation of other patients.

It is easy for the official who is showing a ward to a visitor to state authoritatively and to believe that the chronic psychotic patient is oblivious of her surroundings and unable to appreciate the interior decoration and layout of a ward. This is hardly ever true. One should always question such an assertion, preferably aloud.

That many chronic psychotic patients do appreciate all that goes on has been shown over and over again. Drab surroundings communicate to the patient the idea that 'nothing matters' which fosters the apathy being produced by other pressures. Butler (1887) repeatedly pointed out the importance of scrutinizing the hospital environment to find and remove whatever is depressing or disturbing. He insisted that a cheerful sympathetic atmosphere and aesthetic approach are essential for many patients. His goal was to make hospital wards as home-like as possible (Bockoven, 1956).

8. Loss of Prospects Outside the Institution

After admission to a mental hospital, as time goes by the prospects of finding a place to live, a job to work at and friends to mix with diminish rapidly. It is difficult to persuade patients that the tremendous effort to re-enter the world outside is worth the gain. Many patients say they never wish to leave hospital: 'I'm quite happy jogging along here, Doctor,' or 'Leave me alone, Doctor, I'm not well enough to manage outside,' or 'Nobody wants me—they haven't got room.' Similar difficulties have been encountered with patients who have spent a long time in tuberculosis sanatoria (Pugh, 1955).

On a lesser scale similar attitudes, doubts and difficulties arise with demobilization of some members of the armed forces, especially long-service men. Resettlement is often a painful and difficult business.

The problem of accommodation is at present (1976) extremely difficult. Unless a patient returns to his family or rooms fairly quickly the chances are that he will find great difficulty in getting back. This is not true in all cases, but in many it seems as though the place he leaves in the community to enter hospital gradually seals up. A woman whose husband is admitted to hospital for a long time may have to take a lodger to help keep the home going, or may have an affair more for comfort than lust or wickedness. A man whose wife is admitted to hospital may have to get a housekeeper to look after the children and she may interpret her duties somewhat liberally so that there may be no home for the patient to come back to, even though completely recovered. Rooms are expensive and not easy to come by, especially as many local authorities will not allow their tenants to sublet. Some landladies, although professing willingness to cooperate, are too nervous to take in a mental patient. Patients themselves will not always accept anything that comes, and often find difficulty in tolerating noise from occupants of other rooms and joining in the give-and-take of communal life. Some patients do not wish to return to relations—some seem to fare better if they do not go back to them.

These difficulties of living outside the institution, so well known to the psychiatric social worker, seem to be communicated to the patient and in some cases are enhanced by the memory of unfortunate experiences before admission. Patients may also be put off by the horror stories brought back by patients a little more advanced on the ladder of rehabilitation who tend to paint a discouraging picture of the outside world to absolve themselves from failure. Many patients have lost confidence in their ability ever to work again. Some remark they cannot think how they ever managed to get up and go to work daily, others feel nobody will employ them— they are too old or incompetent or feel too tired most of the time. The conviction that they will never be able to earn a living or find economic security persuades them to accept the institution as a permanency—especially if life is not too unpleasant, as in the case of ward workers who are often accorded special privileges and paid a small wage.

A further fear that some patients have is loneliness. They can see little prospect beyond living in a room with no one to talk to or to visit. The promise of social clubs, visits and support from psychiatric social workers and out-patient clinic facilities does not usually overcome these forebodings, and the need to accept the institution as a permanent home is again emphasized. Often they are all too true. One patient said: 'You don't make friends when you get older.' An intelligent non-mental patient who had spent a year in a tuberculosis sanatorium described her trepidation at the thought of leaving, her inability to make decisions, her irrational fear of re-entering society: 'You are no longer in the swim; even with close friends, they allude to things that have happened while you were away, you have to elbow your way in. It is a terrifying experience and needs a lot of courage.'

Many other prospects seem poor to the patient. Admission to hospital may seem the final confirmation that there is no longer any chance of fulfilling their ambitions, be they of marriage, children, social advancement, acquisition of wealth or position. It is not easy to achieve one's identity and role in this life—where a role is defined as learned behaviour in relation to other people. This role, as a husband, wife, father, mother, neighbour, employee, member of different groups and so forth, disappears on admission to hospital. It seems that with this realization many people resign themselves too completely to their lot, becoming more apathetic than the situation demands.

Chapter 4

Treatment of Institutional Neurosis

Various aspects of the treatment of institutional neurosis have been described in articles reprinted from *The Lancet* in the booklet *In the Mental Hospital* (1957), in the books *From Custodial to Therapeutic Patient Care in Mental Hospitals* by Greenblatt et al. (1955) and *The Mental Hospital* by Stanton and Schwartz (1954), and discussed at various meetings at the Royal Society of Medicine and of the Royal Medico-psychological Association. From these sources the concept or construct of institutional neurosis was derived.

Starting with a severe institutional neurosis, possible improvement may conveniently be divided into seven arbitrary steps ending with the patient independent of hospital. The chart (*Fig.* 1) shows the stages through which a patient may be helped to ascend. A given patient may be at any one of the arbitrary stages on the chart and may ascend several stages at a time. For example, Mrs P. C., aged 49 years, admitted with paranoid schizophrenia, had been in hospital for 17 years and had sat around doing nothing for years. A ward sister developed an interest in her, lent her a sewing machine and invited her home. Her son aged 22 years, whom she had not seen since he was 5, was traced and began to visit her regularly. After 9 months the patient left hospital, successfully remarried, and lived happily in the West of England for many years.

This patient jumped from sitting around doing nothing to moving to a quieter ward and working part time, and then was discharged from hospital to her relatives and was no longer attached to hospital in any way except that she wrote every 6 months to let the hospital know how she was. Other patients may not be able to improve more than one stage. Exceptionally a patient may be encountered who may not be able to improve at all.

The purpose of a ladder chart is to simplify communication to attendants with varied backgrounds and vocabulary attainment. Provision of such a pictorial representation to convey a series of abstract notions is dangerous as is most reification but, it is

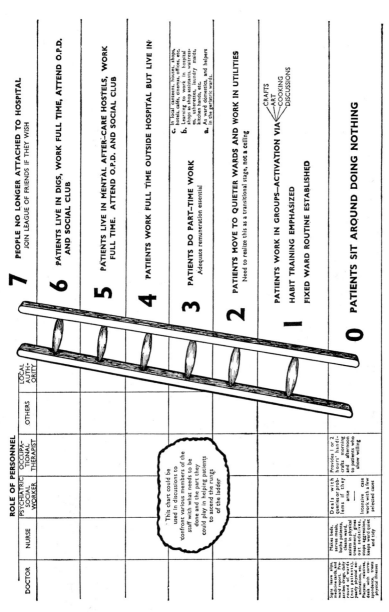

Fig. 1.—Chart showing arbitrary stages in rehabilitating patients with institutional neurosis.

WHAT CAN BE DONE?   WHO SHOULD DO WHAT?

ACTIVITIES NECESSARY TO COMBAT INSTITUTIONAL NEUROSIS	PSYCHIATRIST WARD DOCTOR	NURSE GRADE n-8 to n	ATTENDANT (SRN)	OCCUPATIONAL THERAPIST	SOCIAL WORKER	PSYCHOLOGIST
1. Re-establishment of patients' contacts with the outside world						
2. Provision of daily sequence of: Useful occupations Recreations Social events						
3. Eradication of: Brutality Browbeating Harshness Teasing						
4. Alteration of attitudes of: Attendants Administrators Nurses Doctors Others						
5. Encourage and make it possible for a patient to have: Friends Possessions Personal events						
6. Reduction of drugs						
7. Provision of a homely, friendly, permissive ward atmosphere with pleasant interior decoration						
8. Prospects of: A job Accommodation Friends outside hospital						
9. Recruitment, education, arousal of enthusiasm, and maintenance of morale of staff caring for patients						

Fig. 2.—Cross-reference chart confronting individual members of staff with their role and contribution in combating institutional neurosis. Each member of the discussion group should identify himself or herself under one of the vertical columns and enter a +, + + or + + + opposite the activities where they can help.

MANIFEST CONCERN?   CARRY OUT THE TASK?

ADMINISTRATOR DIRECTOR OR SUPERINTENDENT	BUSINESS SUPPLIES OFFICER	ENGINEER, BUILDING STAFF, PLUMBER, ETC.	FRIENDS VOLUNTEERS	GOVERNING COMMITTEE	OTHER COMMITTEES	LOCAL AUTHORITY (COMMUNITY WORKERS)	RELATIONS	FAMILY PHYSICIANS	OTHER*

* Chaplain, switchboard operator, members of legislative bodies.
(The actual contribution made by any individual is best arrived at by himself or herself in group discussion. This chart enables a group leader to confront various employees concerned with the mentally ill with the roles they could play. When an employee cannot identify his contribution, others are usually quick—maybe too quick—to point out what should be done.)

submitted, if properly used can be helpful in putting across the possibilities of rehabilitation and the part employees could play.

Treatment may be considered in association with aetiological factors:

1. Re-establishment of patients' contacts with the outside world.

2. Provision of a daily sequence of useful occupations, recreations, and social events 14 hours a day, 7 days a week.

3. Eradication of brutality, browbeating and teasing.

4. Alteration of staff attitudes to amiability, acceptance and assistance. This cannot be done by giving orders and is not usually achieved by psychoanalysis.

5. Encourage and make it possible for a patient to have friends and possessions, and enjoy personal events.

6. Reduction of drugs where possible.

7. Provision of a friendly, homely, permissive atmosphere.

8. Make the patient aware that there are prospects of accommodation, work, friendship, and a more satisfying way of life outside the institution.

Having arrived at these objectives, it is necessary to confront all concerned in the treatment of psychiatrically ill people with two questions: (1) What can be done to achieve these objectives? (2) Who should do what? (*Fig.* 2.)

Outside Hospital

Since a psychiatric service begins and should end outside hospital, both institutional and local authority staff in the community should ask themselves these same questions—'What can be done?' 'Who should do what?' They need to become aware of the social implications and the dangers of admission to hospital. All too often admission is resorted to as an expedient way of solving a difficult social situation which cannot be rapidly and easily dealt with by community care. Often admission could have been avoided by judicious earlier intervention. Great wisdom and knowledge are needed to marshal and manage appropriate contributions from public welfare services to enable a person to float in the community rather than sink in an institution.

Hospital Staff

A cross-reference chart with objectives written on the left-hand side and members of the staff across the top (*Fig.* 2) serves as a useful guide for discussion. Small groups of 6 to 10 employees can see from this chart what needs to be done to correct various factors and how they can best help to do it. I have found that for this first meeting or so members of such a group are busy telling what other members of the staff should be doing. The group leader needs great tact and persistence to get each member to finally see for himself or herself what he or she can do personally.

In any ward or hospital it is important to examine critically what is happening before attempting to make alterations. Unless influential senior staff are behind the changes that have to be made little can be done. To try to destroy the influence of senior people rather than involve and work through them is poor strategy, and causes strife, obstruction and unhappiness. There is no need to destroy existing administration in order to bring about changes.

CORRECTION OF THE VARIOUS FACTORS

1. Re-establishment of Patients' Contacts

With (a) the ward and employees; (b) the hospital and hospital functions; (c) the patient's home and catchment area.

Re-establishment of patients' contacts with the outside world starts in the ward. The patient is usually aware of what goes on but makes no meaningful communication. The ward doctor needs to talk to the patient for some minutes every day. The easiest way of doing this is to walk round the ward and sit beside the patient, or sit under a table with him, or sit on the foot of the bed. Content of talk should be straightforward and good humoured. It is desirable to criticize patients' behaviour and appearance good naturedly, for this not only acts as a gentle influence persuading them to conform in a more socially acceptable way, but, perhaps more important, shows them that they matter. It may be months before any flicker of response occurs confirming that contact has been made. This few minutes' contact from the ward doctor needs to be supplemented by similar individual attention from an attendant and from the head nurse. Similarly, a brief word from visitors to the ward or administrative staff when they are doing their rounds helps to confirm the impression that the patient matters.

More intensive individual attention was given to 26 catatonic patients by Roland (1948) and this produced improvement in 24 of them. Of these 24, 12 who had been mute began to talk and 6 returned home after 6 months. Among the factors considered important were:

    i. Patience and alertness on the part of the instructor in adjusting techniques to meet the needs of the individual patient.

    ii. The development of ability to sustain attention.

    iii. Study of the patient's background gives important clues that aid bringing him back to reality.

Looking back it seems probable that Roland's efforts cured the institutional neurosis that was developing or had developed but did not affect underlying catatonic schizophrenia. Bennet (1955) developed an intensive rehabilitation programme for a group of schizophrenic patients and achieved significant improvement after 1 year. Again, it is unlikely that the basic schizophrenic illness was affected. The secondary institutional neurosis was cured to some extent.

Contact with the ward is furthered by forming patients into groups of 6 to 10 under the charge of one attendant, 'the primary therapist,' who concentrates on teaching the patients in her group the pattern of behaviour in the ward. They learn to do things together and also to re-acquire simple skills such as combing their hair, dressing themselves, making their beds, eating at table, etc.

A large notice-board about 8 ft × 5 ft (2·5 m × 1·5 m) with details of all ward functions and facilities is essential. The attendant takes her group of patients to this board every day and reads out the notices and discusses the possibilities even if it has to be a soliloquy. In this way the attendant and the patient have a basis for 'what to do'. Details of physical exercise, games and deportment classes to combat the institutional posture should be displayed together with the rest of the daily and weekly ward routine. (By ward routine is meant a regular sequence of events, working, recreational and social, 14 hours a day, 7 days a week.) It can be seen that an attendant needs to be with her group for at least 3 months and needs to understand clearly the aims in view in order to be therapeutically potent—in order to help the patient to establish a more active contact with the ward events and situations.

Contact with the people, events and situations in a ward is essential but is only a first step. Contact with the hospital in general is desirable and may be fostered by inter-ward parties, by ward socials for relatives, by dances, by visits to a central café and hospital shops, by working in various departments and so on. Attention needs to be given to the patients' appearance—hair style, face, clothes, hands, stockings and shoes—before they are encouraged to leave the ward. Many patients understand why they have not been included in a group for a walk if they are told they are too untidy. 'I wish you could come, but I can't take you out like that,' said one sister who has had outstandingly good results in a rehabilitation drive. New spectacles or even cataract operations may be required by some patients, while others may begin to make contact and take interest if a hearing aid is provided. The work of the ophthalmologist, optician and E.N.T. specialist will increase.

When improvement of appearance and social graces allows, patients can be taken in small groups for walks into the local village, bus rides to nearby towns, and on shopping expeditions to their home district. It is surprising how much many enjoy riding on a bus and paying their own fare again—car journeys and coach journeys are not useful as everything is done for the patient. The attendant needs to restrain herself from helping unless she sees her charges are going to the wrong bus stop or are about to get on the wrong bus, etc. Individual enterprise must be fostered and not smothered by doing things the patient might be able to do. *The art of the psychiatric nurse or attendant is to judge when to intervene to preserve the patient's dignity and confidence without robbing him of the chance to do things for himself.*

Open doors are possible on most, probably all, wards. This lets patients feel less imprisoned and increases their dignity and self-respect. Open doors are highly potent weapons in treating institutional neurosis (Bell, 1955).

Visits home need careful planning. The psychiatric social worker plays a most important role in sorting out the complexities of the home situation, allaying the relatives' fears and advising the doctor when the optimum time would be for a first visit and its duration, i.e. when children are at school or someone is away on holiday. It may be desirable for an attendant to accompany the patient in some instances, but if the relative has been brought into the patient's hospital life this may not be necessary. An important function of an attendant accompanying a patient home may be to restrain the relatives from doing everything for her. Patients have complained about the solicitous attentions of relatives which make them feel unnecessary and a nuisance. One patient said: 'They wouldn't even let me make the tea.'

Liaison between the mental hospital nurse and a public health nurse carrying out the activities suggested by Shalit (1948) is profitable. The need for expansion of Public Health in the field of mental disorders is generally recognized (Carse et al., 1958; MacMillan, 1958), and the cooperation of district nurses in the patient's catchment area with mental hospital nurses in dealing with the patient's family would seem advantageous. Training graduate nurses for such duties has been advocated by Barrett (1948).

It would seem to be helpful for the patient to start making contact with the day hospital and therapeutic social club in the catchment area before going on leave so that further visits when away from hospital will be facilitated. Having gone there in a group with a nurse once or twice the patient knows where to go, when to go and what to expect. It is helpful for many people to make a new venture in the company of someone they know. It seems likely that once the ice has been broken further attendance will be less of an ordeal.

Apart from visits home the patient needs to be encouraged to write letters to relatives regularly. Notepaper, pens and ink need to be offered and a regular time set aside for letter writing. Public telephones for outgoing calls are useful since the nurse can often persuade visitors to go to a prearranged number to take a telephone call from a patient at a given time. It might be important to limit the number and duration of such calls so that all patients might share the facilities and the relatives' tolerance be not exhausted by endless tirades or wrangling. More public telephones would be needed in most mental hospitals. Relatives, friends and members of a League of Friends may be encouraged to write to patients and to send them birthday cards and Christmas cards each year. Telephone calls to patients in the hospital seem an attractive idea but the risk of their replacing visits would need to be borne in mind.

Visiting could be made much easier by encouraging it at any time any day between 9.0 a.m. and 9.0 p.m. This has been in operation at Severalls Hospital since 1960 and few difficulties resulted. The usual objections about interference with nursing routines, etc. have proved to be groundless (Barton et al., 1961). The psychiatric social worker might arrange for fares to be paid. Transport clubs could be arranged and perhaps a hospital coach for evening visits, picking relatives up in the catchment area and returning them. Visitors would be asked to take part where possible in the patients' activities, but not to interrupt the patients' working hours. It would be useful if a patient could have a guest to a meal, say, twice a week—and the nurse could always point out the benefit to the patient if she were taken out for a meal at the next visit. Relatives need to be sought out by the psychiatric social worker and persuaded to visit. The most unlikely people become interested and visitors may have a profound effect on institutional neurosis. It could be helpful in some cases if the relatives could be persuaded to form a rota of visits so that the patient had someone to look forward to regularly, but, at the same time, the visitors were not exhausted by a tedious expensive bus journey, a long walk inside the hospital grounds, and a dubious welcome on the ward by patient and nursing staff. Similarly a rota of relatives to whom the patient could go in turn might increase the patient's contact, but such a scheme would only supplement and not replace one regular visitor and one regular weekend host. Furthermore, to impose such arrangements without willing agreement or to manipulate relatives into accepting them is of dubious value.

Relatives encouraged to enter the therapeutic team with the sister and the doctor might well be persuaded to meet the patient in the Therapeutic Social Club in the catchment area once a fortnight.

Figure 3 shows a schematic representation of possible modes of keeping the patient in contact with the outside world. It should be noted that the foregoing are suggestions only. They are not exhaustive and many doctors, social workers and nurses have introduced these and other measures with success.

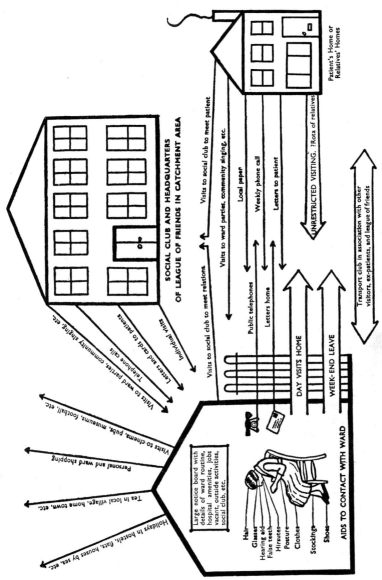

Fig. 3.—Contact with the outside world.

The re-establishment of contact, although greatly facilitated by such measures, requires above all an awareness of its importance by everyone concerned with the patient—from members of the highest administrative authority, the Hospital Management Committee, medical and nursing staff, relatives and members of the League of Friends and the Health Authorities in the patient's home district. The drive necessary to translate these practical measures into action needs to come from social worker, nursing and medical staff. 'The will is what matters most.' It is surprising how often the seemingly most inert people become enthusiastic and active in rehabilitation programmes. It requires great wisdom to prevent them becoming estranged from other members of the staff and they need self-restraint to ensure the necessary changes are generally realized to be a group project and not one person 'going it alone'. Doctors, nurses or social workers who have 'got the rehabilitation bug' may lose self-criticism and be unable to evaluate the results of the measures they introduce. Thus many reports published are of dubious value. In some the observations are doubtful, whilst in others there are enthusiastic schemes advocated by their innovators which have not been impartially or sufficiently tried to assess their merit. 'A judicious distrust and wise scepticism are the sinews of understanding' (Epicharmus).

2. Provision of Daily Sequence of Useful Occupations, Recreations and Social Events 14 Hours a Day, 7 Days a Week

Individual patient programmes

Each patient needs a well-thought-out timetable of activities and idlenesses. To do nothing all day, every day, by default because of insufficiency or indolence of staff is unsatisfactory. Equally unsatisfactory is regimenting patients through a ritual of activities they dislike—such as endlessly making felt toys—to satisfy an accrediting body or visiting inspectors. To do nothing after due scrutiny of a patient's symptoms, personality strengths and weaknesses is satisfactory, providing the quality of the patient's life, the progress of his symptoms and the purpose of his inactivity are reviewed every month by the psychiatrist, every week by the head nurse and every day by his primary therapist. (For description of primary therapist, *see below*.)

The different constituents of a patient's programme of activities and idlenesses should take place at different places. Some should be in the ward, some in different parts of the hospital and others outside the hospital in the patient's home or community.

It is disadvantageous to organize the whole of a patient's programme on his ward. A change of scene often acts like a tonic and variety should be aimed at. Unfortunately it costs money to move a patient from one place to another. It takes manpower and manpower is expensive—more so if employees have to be paid overtime. In providing a programme for an individual, pains should be taken to ensure that the events organized command his interest and enthusiasm. To do this the patient should be asked what he finds worth while doing, what he enjoys, what interests him and so forth. Further evidence may be given by relatives, friends, social workers, psychologists through preference tests and vocational guidance tests, and from other patients.

In some patients no interests can be discerned. For them trial and error is the only approach, using such primary activities as carpentry, cooking, moulding clay, painting, music, bowls, splashing round in the shallow end of a swimming pool (temperature 85 °F, 30 °C), walks—not in an institutional crocodile—visits to the patient's home town or home providing prior arrangements have been made, and so forth.

A personal programme of appointments, therapy sessions and events has to be built up gradually for patients with institutional neurosis. *Figure 4* is a printed card issued to patients every week or so. Whenever possible a patient should help to fill in and take care of his own card and be responsible for keeping it up to date and getting himself to his appointments on time.

Ward programmes

Distinct from, but complementary to, the patient's individual programme is the ward timetable.

A ward with a population of 40 or 50 patients needs to be divided up into 6 or 7 groups of 6 or 7 patients, each of whom is assigned to a 'primary therapist', who is an attendant, a nurse, an assistant nurse, a medical student or a social work student who is willing and able to take on the task. The primary therapist is the patient's friend, counsellor and advocate. She takes the role of foster mother to members of her group, ensures that their grooming is passable, their clothes are marked with their name, and that they have an individual programme which includes participation in the ward programme. It is vital that a primary therapist meets with her patients as a group for at least 10 minutes but preferably 30–40 minutes every day. She pays attention to them individually at other times. Although paternalistic at first, her relationship should reduce to that of a peer as often and for as long as possible. Each group needs to appoint a 'deputy primary therapist' who keeps the meeting going if the primary therapist is absent, is called away or does not turn up for the group meeting at the time scheduled on the ward programme. Primary therapists have to meet together with the head nurse or psychiatrist two or three times a week.

33

PROGRAM OF APPOINTMENTS, THERAPY SESSIONS AND EVENTS
(Always write in place and name of Physician, Professional, Group Leader or Volunteer)

TIME	MONDAY	TUESDAY	WEDNESDAY	THURSDAY	FRIDAY	SATURDAY
			B R E A K F A S T			
9:00-10:00						
10:00-11:00						
11:00-12:00						
			L U N C H			
1:00- 2:00						
						SUNDAY
2:00- 3:00						
3:00- 4:00						
			E V E N I N G M E A L			
5:00- 7:00						
OTHER EVENING EVENTS						

Inside cover—Timetable to be filled in with patient's ward, hospital and community appointments.

PROGRAM

ROCHESTER PSYCHIATRIC CENTER
1600 South Avenue
Rochester, N.Y.
Director: Russell Barton, M.D.

Rochester Psychiatric Center is a facility run by the New York State Department of Mental Hygiene.

We are glad to have you with us. You can expect us to try to understand your trouble and do all we can to help.

In turn, we expect your co-operation in keeping your appointments and therapy sessions, in accepting reasonable restrictions and complying with reasonable requests.

Together we can make a difference. Alone, maybe, neither of us can do much.

The Staff of Rochester Psychiatric Center

ROCHESTER
RPC
PSYCHIATRIC CENTER

People care and People are Cared
Where   For

NAME _____

Unit Chief _____.

Primary Therapist _____.

Back cover   *Front cover*

Fig. 4.—Patient's personal programme card. Appointments are entered by the patient aided by her primary therapist. Unit chief is the consultant psychiatrist responsible for treatment.

The ward programme should dovetail with the groups' activities. Two groups may use the bathrooms and washing facilities while another two groups are making their beds and tidying their living area and another group is laying tables for breakfast. This starts the day by confronting the patient with useful activity such as would be required at home. Such a shift system prevents the cramped and squalid washing and lavatory facilities provided in most hospitals being overcrowded and transforms washing, grooming, shaving and dressing to a more agreeable and pleasant experience as the first event of the day.

SHAVING, GROOMING, TOILET, DRESSING AND SELF-CARE

Electric razors have eased the problem of shaving and the danger of razor blades. Blunt blades and awkward attendants made shaving a most uncomfortable ordeal in former days. Right from the start of a programme of rehabilitation great care and attention should be paid to the patient's personal appearance. Shaving, regular showers or baths (which requires adequate supplies of hot water, easily available showers and bath towels) and well-fitting clothes are necessary. The supply of clothes should be arranged as in a clothes shop.

Men patients should be taken to the shop to choose or be helped to choose 2 shirts, a suit, a pair of trousers, a jacket, 2 ties, 3 pairs of underpants, 3 pairs of socks, 2 pairs of shoes, a pair of bedroom slippers, an overcoat, pyjamas and a bathrobe.

The equipment for living must be properly fitted—sleeves and trousers cut to the right length and shirts not too tight when buttoned round the neck.

Women patients require 2 pretty frocks, a cardigan, 2 petticoats, 3 pairs of knickers, 2 brassières, 3 pairs of pantihose, 2 pairs of shoes, 2 nightdresses, a pair of bedroom slippers, a bathrobe, a coat and maybe a hat. These should be selected from a hospital shop (set out like a ladies' fashion shop in a local High Street) with assistance when necessary.

Name tabs should be sewn or stuck on to all garments by the patient, or his relatives or attendant with him present, and the clothes and shoes then stored in the combination wardrobe chest of drawers/ ward partition with mirror described on page 59.

A patient's clothes should be dry cleaned and pressed regularly, shoes should be cleaned and shirts and socks laundered as often as necessary. To achieve this the ward requires a washing machine, a spin dryer and an ironing room for use of patients. Patients may not be able to do these things for themselves for some time, but should always accompany the clothes to the laundry room and be asked to help the visiting relative, the nurse or attendant to carry out these tasks.

Payment for clothes should be subsidized where necessary but the patient should be asked to contribute and encouraged to pay weekly instalments as he would if he lived outside.

This basic wardrobe and toilet preparations such as soap, shampoo, shaving soap and cosmetics should be kept topped up, and every encouragement and assistance given to patients to help them to look clean and attractively groomed and dressed.

Relatives should be urged to help patients deal with their laundry, dry cleaning, name-tabbing and so forth. The concept that a hospital is totally responsible for management and care is fallacious. An enlisted group of relatives can make an enormous contribution to a programme for chronic institutionalized patients. The participation of relatives and friends should be actively solicited and positively encouraged. Admission to hospital should not bludgeon helping hands or deter acquaintances from doing kindly acts which spell affection and concern.

REDEVELOPMENT OF SOCIAL SKILLS AND GRACES

At first a group of 6 or 7 regressed patients should sit in a small circle of easy chairs every day for 30 or 40 minutes with their primary therapist who should be assigned to them and they to her for a period of at least 3 months. The primary therapist could read a short paragraph from *Time*, *Newsweek* or the local or morning paper and then ask questions of each patient in turn, preferably prefixing the surname with 'Mr', 'Mrs' or 'Miss'. Attempts at *bonhomie* by use of Christian names often make patients, especially new patients, uncomfortable. Exceptions are sometimes desirable, for example in groups of adolescents. The experienced employee will feel comfortable using surnames or Christian names but should be sufficiently sensitive and sympathetic to discern which is the optimum usage.

Taking patients to the hospital shop, the hospital library, a hospital exhibition of pictures and discussing everyday matters and what is seen, asking the patient: 'What is your opinion about . . . ?' 'Do you like . . . ?' 'Have you tried?' and so forth, sometimes allowing a silence of a few seconds if the patient is mute, sometimes remarking: 'I wish you could tell me whether you like . . .', 'I would like to know what you think' and sometimes answering the question after a silence by saying 'I wonder if you feel like I do, I like . . .'— these questions are samples of the repertoire needed to engage the patient's attention and interest in simple social transactions.

An intelligent volunteer can often work wonders in developing social skills, especially one of the same age-group and background as the patient. Trips to museums, to zoos, to local exhibitions, inviting or being invited to other wards, other clubs, trips to the seaside preferably by public transport, attendance for worship in local churches will help to further social skills and poise.

The development of more sustained and complicated activities stressing and rewarding appropriate reactions, remarking on inadequate responses and faulty behaviour, should be continued, progress being reviewed and noted every week or so. Each patient who is a member of the attendant's group should be discussed by the attendant with the psychiatric nurse overlooking the treatment programme regularly. Attendants need a great deal of encouragement and reassurance—but not to be patronized.

COOKING AND HOUSEHOLD MANAGEMENT

The chronic regressed mentally ill woman may not have made a cup of tea, boiled an egg, baked a pasta or prepared a cup of soup for many years. A household management unit with work surfaces, gas and electric stoves and washing-up facilities is invaluable. Few patients can resist a bowl with flour, butter, milk, raisins and other ingredients.

As the art of cookery is achieved, a meal should be prepared and eaten by the patients doing the cooking; they should also lay the table, have the privilege of inviting one or two guests and being responsible for the washing up. As progress occurs, patients should be encouraged to go out to the grocer's shop or supermarket, at first accompanied by an attendant, to purchase the ingredients. This acquaints them with modern prices, preparation of food and so forth. Such expeditions should not be made at rush hours or peak periods, when tempers of shopkeepers are short, until patients have made considerable progress and can cope with other people's hostility and rudeness.

Washing machines, spin driers, sewing machines and so forth will enable a patient to complete her experience.

RECREATION

Early on, moulding clay to make an ashtray, drawing random lines on a piece of paper pinned on an easel, selecting a few shapes enclosed by some of the lines and then painting the pattern produced in different colours will be a first step towards more complex recreational activity. Rewards are essential. Later on painting, modelling, photography, music, theatrical productions, whist drives, dances, barbecues, train trips can be organized.

A useful landmark in a ward timetable is an evening of community singing from 7.0 p.m. to 9.0 p.m. Relatives may be invited to come along or possibly a volunteer or member of the League of Friends may organize it. I have found it useful for the pianist to start off with the chorus of a well-known song such as 'Just a Song at

37

Twilight' (not the verse) or 'Raindrops Keep Falling on My Head' and to have copies of the words in big type handed out. A few patients may be chosen to sing a special number such as 'On Wings of Song'. Men invited to these sing-songs make them more popular. Gradually the routine organization becomes established and the event a fixture. At this stage a second evening activity from 7.0 p.m. to 9.0 p.m. could be introduced such as a games evening with draughts, ludo, whist or bingo.

The ward timetable can include a weekly ward dance or a dancing lesson from 7.0 p.m. to 10.0 p.m. As patient's appearance, posture and behaviour improve guests can be invited from other wards or from outside the hospital. Attendants soon understand that they dance with patients and not with each other or relatives—it is surprising how soon it becomes difficult to tell who is a patient (Carstairs et al., 1955). Attendance at a monthly hospital dance should be restricted to those who have made adequate progress at the ward dances.

Painting can be started by getting a group of 6 patients and a nurse to sit down in front of a board with paper on it while a demonstrator paints a picture in front of them doing each step at a time and making sure they follow it with the nurse's help. Once they have learned to use brushes and acrylic paints and keep their colours clean they can be encouraged to copy pictures or paint whatever they wish.

PHYSICAL EXERCISE

Daily physical exercise is necessary to most people. All human beings tend to become sluggish if physically inactive and the benefit of regular engagement in gentle physical exercise by people with institutional neurosis may be related to this.

The head nurse needs to establish a time on the ward each day, except Sunday, for this activity. Patients and staff can clear a space in the dayroom. Most regressed patients should be required to participate in a simple task such as walking up and down the day room, or walking round in a circle to music with one hand holding a thick rope with both ends joined. Walking along a straight line balancing a book on the head may help improve posture—it is important that attendants join in to prevent a 'them' and 'us' attitude and distinction being emphasized. Hula hoops are very effective in helping to kindle interest. The nurse, taking a patient's hand, swings the hoop on her own wrist at first, then, when the patient has absorbed the rhythm and movement necessary to keep the hoop circling on the arm, transfers it to the patient's arm. Eventually the patient may be able to swing the hoop on her arm and two patients can keep a hoop going without help. Swinging the hula hoop on the body is much more difficult and not worth pushing, unless patients wish to try—seeing members of the staff or other patients trying, and occasionally succeeding, is often an incentive. The object of these simple exercises is merely to obtain interest and participation—there is no point in patients becoming expert hula hoopers. Participation should be rewarded with a sweet (not for diabetics), a cigarette (not for non-smokers), participation in a special tea, praise and so forth. Physical rewards such as candy and cigarettes should be replaced by encouraging words and smiles and praise as improvement occurs, for cigarettes cause cancer and sweets obesity.

As soon as participation in a very simple activity has been obtained, attempts should be made to engage the patient in a slightly more complicated task. It is vital that the task should only be slightly more complicated. Little steps are the rule and the proverb 'the longest journey starts with one step' the philosophy. Group exercises, such as are devised by health and beauty movements for women, foster the idea that they redistribute the fat on the body, removing it from the buttocks. This is a harmless delusion, shared by the patients' sisters in the community, but it provides motivation to join in and should not be discounted. Dieting at this stage is undesirable, but reduction of doses of phenothiazines, which cause obesity in most people, may be very helpful in more ways than one.

Other physical activities are walks, swimming, games, gymnastics, dancing, gardening, mixing concrete (using handmixers, not motorized), and moulding kerb stones, paving blocks, concrete bird-baths and 'gnomes for gardens of suburban homes'. Work and tiring exercise are often a successful combination for aggressive younger patients—and those who are mentally retarded.

Note that throwing balls about in a day room or sitting room is out of place and that chronically regressed patients should not be expected to participate in complicated games. In the first stages, participation may have to be gently insisted upon.

As participation in one form of activity is accomplished, further slightly more complicated programmes can be initiated until full-scale activities outside the ward such as basketball, Highland dancing, track events, skiing or riding are enjoyed. Dr Bickford of de la Pole Hospital in Yorkshire made horses available for selected patients to learn to ride. He felt that the increase in social esteem arising from being able to ride a horse compensated, to some extent, for the loss of esteem incurred by being a patient in a mental hospital.

Work

Work is an essential aspect of existence and most people measure themselves by the work they do for themselves or their communities.

Early work programmes include scraping, sandpapering and painting ward chairs in bright colours, making envelopes for X-rays, books of drawing paper for children and Christmas decorations, and packing screws in plastic bags. Such programmes are best introduced on the ward. Participation should be encouraged by giving sweets or cigarettes as an immediate reward and a small amount of money, at the end of a session, according to productivity. The possession of money then requires a trip to a hospital shop or canteen to spend it. It is important that the patient goes to the shop and is allowed to spend his money.

There is always the danger that when a regressed patient successfully participates in a routine, it will not easily be relinquished by staff or patients. As improvement occurs, regimentation needs to become less and less until the patient, just before leaving hospital, does as much for herself in the way of personal arrangements and organization as she will do outside.

Some patients are loath to leave hospital if they have a hospital job, freedom and friends in their ward and at work. This does not seriously hamper discharge. A few weekends out of hospital, a week in an hotel or a camping coach and arrangements to share an apartment change a patient's mind more surely than argument.

When successful participation in a ward programme has been achieved, work in a sheltered hospital workshop should be attempted. The patient should be helped to get ready at first and after a few days be asked to clock in and out as customary in industrial practice. Although some allowances should be made, especially early on in the rehabilitation process, psychiatric patients must be brought to face reality. If they are late, lazy or incompetent they must be told about it and helped to see what and how they need to improve. Foolish concessions will only result in failure when the patient is placed in employment outside, with resulting loss of self-confidence and souring of the labour market. A worksheet, visible to the patient, on which his work is entered together with the piece-rate is essential. At first, half the day's pay may be given at the end of the day to act as more immediate incentive and the rest accumulated and handed out, in the workshop, at the end of the working week.

When successful timekeeping and work habits have been achieved, judicious placement in employment outside the hospital may be tried. The prospective employer or personnel officer should be seen by the patient's social worker. It is advantageous to supply hospital transport to get the patient to work for the first week or so, the patient finding his own way back to the hospital by public transport.

Special provision for early breakfasts and so forth needs to be arranged and it is often helpful to develop a ward or hostel for working patients with special privileges and minimal supervision.

It is unwise to thrust the double burden of a new job and new accommodation on to a patient at the same time. Usually it is wise for the patient to remain in hospital for some weeks after he has obtained work outside. When he is settled at work, managing his own medication and taking care of his own room in the hospital, a gradual move to living outside the hospital should be made. Going home for weekends, having a week's holiday by the sea are a beginning. Living in lodgings, maybe closer to the place of work, for 5 days a week and returning to the hospital for weekends would be a useful intermediary step before finally leaving hospital and attending an out-patient clinic.

Not every patient will be able to scale the series of graded work achievements as outlined. Nor will such a graded series of activities be easy to arrange. Interference, objection and obstruction are to be expected.

Hospital programmes

Ever since hospitals were established in the eighteenth and nineteenth centuries the importance of hospital programmes has been realized. Farms attached to hospitals provided satisfying labour for over 100 years, but a failure by staff at times to utilize them in the treatment of patients (who were used as cheap labour) and irrational decisions by ill-informed authorities—'We are running a hospital not a farm'—resulted in their being sold off, with a loss to the mentally ill of a very valuable source of work situations, physical exercise, open spaces, good meat and fresh fruit.

One or two sheltered workshops, in which 50–100 patients work on manufacturing or packing products can be used to train patients to attend regularly and punctually, to get on with a job and earn some money. So popular were the industrial workshops introduced at Severalls Hospital in 1960 that patients would arrive early, looking forward to a day's work. Patients should be encouraged to clock on and off after attending for a week or so and their pay should be proportionate to the amount of work they do. The industrial rehabilitation workshops in Delft in the Netherlands providing work for mentally ill and retarded people and others are an example of the type of provision that can be made with imagination, foresight and determination.

Although productivity is important, the real purpose of workshops must not be lost sight of—to afford patients experience and incentive to get employment outside hospital.

An art studio to which patients may come to draw, to paint, make pots and fire them in a kiln, or do sculpture is desirable. The object is not to produce works of art or develop genius but to command the attention and enthusiasm of patients by confronting them with

41

meaningful tasks in the company of others. The hospital timetable should provide 6 sessions a day, morning, afternoon and evening 6 days a week.

Music therapy, which helps patients to appreciate music by listening to records and participating in playing, using Karl Orff instruments (no previous skill is needed), will attract and delight many patients. If a music room is fitted out and the instruments purchased it is not sufficient to have 6 or 7 sessions a week. The hospital programme should provide 30 or 40 sessions weekly so that some 200 or 300 patients can participate. A 'live' piano recital weekly and a monthly concert by several musicians allows patients to hear real music. These concerts will be appreciated more if records of the pieces are listened to on the patient's ward or in the hospital's music centre on two or three occasions before the event.

Hospitals can provide a movie at a centralized location once a week. Patients can act as organizers and ushers and usherettes. Of course, going to a cinema, a theatre or a circus outside hospital is to be preferred but this does not justify jettisoning the hospital programme.

Most hospitals have facilities for religious services for people of different religions. Ward staff should appreciate the comfort and solace afforded by religious belief and not belittle or challenge it. Patients should be encouraged to attend services, and their relatives and friends invited to accompany them.

Other events in a hospital's timetable are dances, a Christmas show, courses of lectures, bring-and-buy sales, aqua festivals at the swimming pool, firework displays on November 5th, and so forth.

The distinction between a patient's individual timetable, a ward timetable and that of the hospital needs to be appreciated and the purpose of each understood. Each requires organization and authority at a different level.

Figure 5 is a timetable to give an idea of some of the many activities that could be aimed at early on in the treatment of a ward of patients disabled by chronic psychoses complicated by institutional neurosis. It is not desirable that patients should be marshalled and regimented in a ceaseless round of activity, to act out a schedule ritualistically. The timetable is presented to offer suggestions for organization and activity. It has been found that replacing idleness with activity reduces aggression, tearing, picking, hoarding, masturbation, and other undesirable behaviour, presumably by providing more socially acceptable things to do. Whatever ward timetable is adopted the events will need to fit in with events in the rest of the hospital. For example, one nurse helped patients to organize a community singing evening the night a concert party was visiting that particular hospital and a dance was being held in a

TIME	MONDAY	TUESDAY	WEDNESDAY	THURSDAY	FRIDAY	SATURDAY	SUNDAY
7–9 a.m.	DRESSING, TOILET, BEDMAKING, AND BREAKFAST ROUTINE						
9.30–11.30 a.m.	Handicrafts Cooking Group gardening Leather-work Group discussion	Handicrafts Dressmaking Sewing Metal-work Wood-work	Handicrafts Weaving Basket-work Group discussion	Handicrafts Typing Printing SHOPPING	Handicrafts Shopping Housework Rug-making Group discussion	Handicrafts Washing clothes Ironing Mending	Church Walks Letter-writing All-day visits to sea, etc.
11.30 a.m.–1.30 p.m.	TOILET AND DINNER ROUTINE						
1.30–4 p.m.	Simple P.T. or Organized games or Relaxation exercises Group discussion SHOPPING	Simple P.T. in ward or garden Movement to music Dancing lessons Dancing practice	VISITORS or LETTER-WRITING or SHOPPING	Organized games or Percussion band or Movement to music or Cooking	Walk and picnic or Visit to local museum or picture gallery or Conversation group with nurse	P.T. in garden or ward Games (inter-ward)	VISITORS
4–5 p.m.	TOILET AND TEA ROUTINE						
5–7 p.m.	Beauty culture Hairdressing and manicure evening	Dance in ward with male patients Barbecue party	Whist drive or Art class Painting, pottery and posters	Talks by patients to patients 'My Home Town' Discussions Debates	GAMES EVENING Draughts, ludo, bingo, billiards, ping-pong tournaments, chess	COMPETITION NIGHT Personal appearance Handicrafts Most progress Simple puzzles	Television
	VISITORS	VISITORS	VISITORS	VISITORS	VISITORS	VISITORS	VISITORS
7–8 p.m.	TOILET AND SUPPER ROUTINE: Patients who need supervision to get undressed, etc., go to bed						
8–10 p.m.	Story-reading to patients by patients or Amateur dramatics	Discussion group or Television or Wireless	Music appreciation Records from library (popular songs) (patients' choice)	Make and mend or Letter-writing	Story-reading or Brains trust or Amateur dramatics	COMMUNITY SINGING	Television followed by brief discussion on what was seen

Fig. 5.—A composite timetable of possible activities to counter institutional neurosis.

43

male ward. Attendance was poor and the evening fell flat. If details of these competing events had been displayed on the notice-board in her ward she might have persuaded more patients to go to the counter-attractions and held her sing-song another day. Subsequent support has been very good. As indicated, the items suggested in such a table are designed to activate patients with a view to getting them on to useful work.

There is a custom in some hospitals for the night staff coming on duty to expect all patients to be in bed. This has become so ingrained that many patients are difficult to keep up after 7.0 p.m. It is necessary to extend the patients' day to 9.0 or 10.0 p.m. or later; the charge nurse may gradually achieve this by asking individual patients to stay up and help with specific projects such as making the tea at a community singing session or collecting the song sheets in the correct piles.

Night staff coming on duty at 8.0 p.m. might hold a painting class until 10.0 p.m. Attendants usually object that they cannot paint until they realize that the object of the session is to activate and prevent idleness and not produce a work of art; to communicate to patients that their time and what they do in it matters, and not that nothing matters and nobody cares whether they are up or in bed. The fact that the nurse wants them to join in a song or to spin a hula hoop on their arm or walk the length of a ward balancing a book on their head communicates to the patients that she is interested. If the nurse sits by the fire reading a paper or talks to another nurse in a foreign language she communicates to the patient an air of indifference to her which favours the development and continuance of institutional neurosis.

Television is useful to fill in some evenings, but there is a danger it will be used too often. It is better to do something than to watch something. If a play is watched on television it is helpful for the night nurse to get a brief discussion going among the patients afterwards— they may talk about the dresses worn, the behaviour of the characters, the acting, and so on. It does not really matter what is discussed. It is participation in the discussion that counts.

3. Eradication of Brutality, Browbeating and Teasing

When the staff on a ward and their supervisors are unable to prevent ill-treatment of patients it follows that they will be unable to prevent intimidation. In most incidents of ill-treatment the victim and any witnesses are threatened with retaliation if they tell their relatives or supervising staff what has happened. In my experience most patients are terrified to report such incidents or to tell tales of teasing and harshness. Thus the majority of incidents of ill-treatment are probably not reported, and are only disclosed by moving the patient

44

to another area, by special interrogation and by questioning patients after discharge.

When an employee is accused of ill-treatment and the matter is investigated, it often boils down to a question of the employee's word against the patient's. Since many psychiatrically ill patients are mentally incompetent their credibility as witnesses is diminished. Furthermore, patients do not always speak the truth. Some are delusional, some harbour pathological grudges and others are psychopathic and make false allegations out of spite calculated to get employees in trouble. Obviously one cannot always take a patient's word. Equally their complaints should never be discounted.

When a physician or a relative inquires about evidence of injuries such as bruises they are usually told either that the patient fell or else that he was assaulted by another patient.

When a full-scale inquiry is carried out, employees will tend to stick together against a common foe. On one occasion, when a police inquiry was made into a mentally retarded patient's death, other patients in the ward, who could possibly have given evidence, had been transferred to another ward and replaced by others unable to give an account of themselves. Newspaper reporters visiting another hospital, following an incident, were invited to talk with the most severely deluded and hallucinated patients who had no idea why a journalist was visiting.

Thus special techniques and experience are necessary to track down ill-treatment and highly skilled administration is necessary to eradicate it.

The competent hospital director (who in my view should be a qualified psychiatrist appointed by the authority to whom the hospital administration is subordinate) and his administration become alerted to the possibility of ill-treatment in many different ways: complaints from relatives, patients or other members of the staff, an unusual number of bruises, fractures and accidents inadequately recorded, excessive drugs supplied, requests from patients to be transferred, unexpected abscondings, unpopularity of a ward for assignment, unusual absenteeism, increased sick leave are a few examples. At this stage inquiry may be unlikely to produce *prima facie* evidence, but an implicit unspoken warning communicated by a visit in the area may deter further occurrences and may encourage witnesses to come forward. No administration, however, can use gossip, rumour and suspicion as a basis for action. The grapevine only tells whom and when and where to question. Such methods of monitoring and correction are much less available to outside authorities and external inspectorates, members of which, if officious or threatening, may unite staff in covering up irregularities by withholding evidence. This is not a fully conscious

45

wilful obstruction of justice, but arises from the usual distaste and distrust that employees who actually work with patients have for outsiders who come in to criticize their performance and fault them and their fellow workers.

Brutality is most likely to be eradicated by the hospital administration itself. The following measures are recommended.

1. Employees' sense of professional purpose and identity should be fostered and the importance of good nature and kindness stressed. This can be done at formal and informal gatherings, dinners, prize-givings, ceremonies, lectures, refresher courses and in-service training programmes. The message has to be sincere and needs a certain amount of subtlety. Simple exhortation to do good is, although worthy, ineffectual. Most people have sympathy for the plight of defenceless mentally ill patients and many staff respond to a drive to cut out ill-treatment and harshness.

2. Senior administrative staff, especially nursing supervisors and medical officers, need to be alerted and enlisted in a continuous programme. They should make a rule on each of their wards that every bruise, every injury and every incident in which ill-treatment is alleged must be the subject of a written report made by staff involved before going off duty. If a bruise or an incident is not reported and recorded, the presumption is that something is being covered up. The report should be short, sharp and to the point giving details such as the patient's name, time, date and place of incident, name of any witnesses, followed by a brief account of incident and any residual evidence—bruising, bleeding, torn clothes, seminal fluid and so forth.

Each incident should be inquired into by the charge nurse or supervising nurse and reported to the medical officer and to the director of nursing.

3. During the day the primary therapist should ask each of her patients how they slept, was all quiet and peaceful on the ward during the night—this is a useful way to start the daily groups. Similarly the head nurse and ward physician should ask patients if they had a good night, what time they got to sleep, who was the attendant or nurse on duty, what time they woke up and so forth. This allows timorous patients to volunteer information about any distressing incidents. Clearly, these inquiries of patients should not be deliberate attempts to fault the nursing staff on duty at night and care must be taken to avoid giving such an impression.

4. Every time a medical officer or supervising nurse sees a patient with a bruise he should ask the head nurse how it happened. Bruises on the forearms of elderly people occur very easily owing to thin skin, loss of elasticity and subcutaneous fat and abnormal capillary fragility. They look disproportionately purple to the trauma

46

causing them and need an experienced nurse or physician to evaluate and interpret them.

5. Members of a management committee or board of governors seeing a patient with a bruise should not self-righteously hold an inquisition on the spot. They should ask the patient her name, check it with the head nurse and later that day write a brief note to the medical officer, sending a copy to the director of nursing, saying something such as:

Dear Dr X,
> While visiting [name of ward] this morning I met a patient named Mrs [patient's name] who had a bruise on [detail of site of bruise]. I felt you would wish me to let you know about it.
>
> Yours sincerely,

To demand a full investigation and written report, to hint that a conclusion of ill-treatment has been jumped to without the facts or to threaten further action will not ultimately be as effective as a simple notification of fact.

6. All employees should be told on joining the hospital staff that brutality, harshness and teasing will not be tolerated. That employees guilty of brutality will be dismissed. Furthermore, it should be impressed upon them that they have an obligation to report such matters to their supervisor. It is as well to say: 'I will not tolerate cruelty or harshness to patients, they are defenceless and already distressed. Most of our staff are kind and agreeable and I am not willing to have their good work discounted and the hospital's reputation dragged in the mud because of the cruelty of a few callous employees.' Note that it is not 'the management' or 'cannot'. It is that *one* person *will* not—even if he could—that gives the employee the message of what is a no–no.

7. All employees are required to apply the minimal physical restraint necessary to a patient who is out of control—assaulting other patients or staff, destroying property, attempting to commit suicide, to abscond and so forth. When more civilized methods fail, physical restraint (minimal) is obligatory and all staff in the vicinity are expected to help. One employee cannot usually manage single-handed. Such restraint does not constitute ill-treatment. When a mêlée arises employees have the right to defend themselves and should be taught before they go on the wards how to control a violent aggressive patient. However, they are not commissioned to use more force than is necessary in securing a patient, they should not be brutal and there is no justification in hitting a patient once he has been secured. The doctrine of minimal physical force necessary to restrain and control a patient should be impressed on all employees, and when allegations of brutality arise here it should be realized the situation is very different from unprovoked

brutality towards a weak and helpless patient. The former may require counselling or a reprimand, the latter dismissal. Whenever physical restraint is used an account should be entered in the nursing notes.

8. In every case where prima facie* evidence of ill-treatment or teasing is found disciplinary action must be taken. The hospital director, after discussion with his senior colleagues and discipline heads, can make this mandatory.

Although never able to achieve it, I have always thought that employees, who should have a written account of the charges and specifications being made, should have a formal, public hearing at which any member of the staff should be entitled to attend (in their own time). Justice should not only be done, but manifestly be seen to be done. Furthermore, employees need to know how decisions are arrived at and why evidence is necessary to get at the truth of a matter. Both a patient and an employee are entitled to justice. Witnesses at disciplinary hearings and hospital inquiries are courageous people, for they may be ostracized by fellow employees and penalized in various ways. These matters should be ventilated in public and employees encouraged to attend so that it becomes clear that ill-treatment is not hospital policy, is not covered up and condoned by hospital authorities who are actively concerned in stamping it out.

9. When unprovoked brutality is proved the employee should be dismissed and the rest of the staff informed by word of mouth by the supervisory staff. Administrative staff should not gloat or feel triumphant when an employee is fired. They should let the staff know that good employees are needed but brutality will not be tolerated.

10. Letters of appreciation of kindness of staff should always be shown to the staff concerned. Care should be taken to see that such letters are not being solicited.

Depending on the effectiveness of the authority delegated to the hospital administration and the nature of the senior and middle management staff, brutality can be drastically reduced in a matter of a few weeks to a few months.

The role of the supra-hospital authority is not to examine and reinvestigate individual complaints so much as to examine the procedures followed by the hospital administration when they received the complaint, the diligence and impartiality used to investigate and deal with it and the final judgement used in arriving at a determination and the penalty awarded.

---

* Prima facie evidence is evidence that would be taken as the fact of a matter unless rebutted by other contradictory evidence.

The majority of investigations and hearings will be inconclusive—but each one held involves employees and communicates very clearly that ill-treatment has no place in hospital practice and is contrary to the therapeutic purpose of the hospital—to cure, to comfort, to make the most of a patient's residual functioning and to do no harm or hurt.

4. Alteration of the Attitude of Professional Staff

C.R.O./12

When replying please quote:
M.15396   (C.R.O.)

Criminal Record Office,
New Scotland Yard,
S.W.1.
16th March, 1949

Sir,

Re S. B., escapee from Mental Hospital
on 6.3.49. Recaptured on 14.3.49.

I am directed by the Commissioner of Police of the Metropolis to refer to the above-named and to aquaint you that she is now registered at this office under the reference quoted.

Yours faithfully,

The Medical Superintendent,
Mental Hospital.

R. M. H.,
Assistant Commissioner.

This letter, concerning a mentally sick woman, is admirable from an administrative point of view. However, its effect on nurses and others who read it is to connect mental illness with the Criminal Record Office. Such an association produces erroneous ideas and a wrong attitude towards mental illness. Any association of crime with mental hospitals is undesirable.

The practice of sending psychopaths who have committed offences to psychiatric hospitals also has a bad effect on the attitude of staff to patients. A few psychopaths may monopolize doctors' and nurses' time, exploit staff shortages and inadequacies, steal from or ill-treat other patients, prevent therapeutic integration of patients, and result in overcautious nursing. Psychopaths are sick people, but admitting them to an ordinary mental hospital is like admitting a case of smallpox to a general hospital or scarlet fever to an obstetric ward. Special institutions with specially trained staff are necessary for the treatment of psychopaths. Nevertheless, some psychopaths can be treated in a psychiatric hospital.

The vital role of nurses in combating institutional neurosis has been discussed by Hunter (1956) and demonstrated by the work of

Bickford (1955) and Cameron et al. (1955). Connolly (1856) stated, 'they [nurses and attendants] may often be considered, indeed, his [the doctor's] best medicines . . .. He confides the most confidential duties to them: he entrusts them with the happiness, by day and night, of all the patients under their special care. To control the violent without anger; to soothe the irritable without weak and foolish concessions; to cheer and comfort the depressed; to guard the imbecile and the impulsive and to direct all' (quoted from Hunter, 1956).

Discussion of the prevailing attitude of hospital staff is always likely to cause offence. Without ventilation, however, it may remain unchanged. It is important not to criticize individuals but to criticize their actions. Ideally, hospital employees would have the opportunity once a week to criticize the psychiatric care they give and to make suggestions of how it could be improved. Criticism of specific examples of actions by named people which are thought to be detrimental are best avoided in general meetings. Unrealistic demands and politics must also be deterred. The problem is the care of a patient in the here and now.

Sometimes discussion and example have no effect on certain individuals, but if they have committed themselves by stating their opinion in their group, therapeutic doubt arises if subsequent events prove them wrong. For example, one charge nurse opposed the unlocking of doors on her ward. She predicted chaos and the perpetration of all sorts of crimes when the patients escaped. She quoted her many years of experience in mental hospitals to support her prediction. One patient, Miss A. G., she stated, was such an escapee she could not be allowed to leave the ward, in a group looked after by a nurse, to attend the occupational therapy hut. The patient was moved to an open ward under an understanding sister. On one occasion she was missing and later had to be collected from a police station. When she discovered she could get leave and was sent home for a weekend she began to make a marked improvement and for the last year she has worked in a sewing room and goes out shopping in near-by towns. None of the ward sister's forebodings has proved correct since the ward doors were unlocked. The ward sister became convinced, albeit reluctantly, that the new approach was worth trying.

The attitude of nursing and attendant staff is easy to modify among junior ranks by example and talks, but it becomes increasingly difficult as the hierarchy is ascended. The need for all types of mental hospital employees to receive educational instruction is stressed by Middleton (1953) in the summary of his very interesting article on the prejudices and opinions of mental hospital employees regarding mental illness. This same need was realized by Brown

(1854), who gave a 'full, if popular, discussion of insanity of the different forms, intelligible by the shrewd and sensible if somewhat illiterate class of persons employed as attendants and nurses'. Some writers have suggested that the rigid hierarchical structure or 'pecking order' of nurses and attendants results in the patient being at the bottom of the scale and thus potentially at the receiving end of all buffets and unpleasantness handed down the nursing hierarchy (Clark, 1958). Each nurse gives orders to her subordinate who in turn gives orders to the attendant below her. The attitude of staff needs to allow a patient to be 'somebody', not, as often in the past, to prove they are nobody.

In order to bring this about the attendant needs to be treated as 'somebody'. Nurses' meetings need to be instituted and the doctors and senior nursing officers need to foster criticism. It helps if senior staff can criticize each other thoughtfully and without animus. If they present a unified front and are always uncritical of each other's point of view the tendency of nurses and attendants is to 'keep mum and play safe'. However, nothing is more destructive of employee morale than personal criticism made maliciously by one senior employee of another, calculated to undermine his reputation. A psychiatrist who tries to relieve his personality defects in this manner, who tries to form a private army of supporters, destroys psychiatric services and requires removing from the hospital. Campaigning by making destructive and defamatory assertions which are untrue and, although paraded as being in the interest of patient care, are actually motivated by personal envy and spite, must be distinguished from sincere concern. After a warning, a senior employee, who continues to try to bolster his ego in this manner, regardless of the needs of patient care, must be removed.

Although unfavourable criticism by employees of their seniors may not be punished overtly in an hierarchical system, nursing personnel may be influenced in many different ways such as moving from one shift or one ward to another, allocation of holiday periods, promotion, or priority in the waiting-list for ward refurnishing or redecoration. Many have the fear of being labelled 'awkward' or 'paranoid' if they are outspoken. Some fear for their testimonials. It is common experience that those who have to be docile and subservient to those above them expect similar behaviour from those beneath them.

This is not to say that a state of anarchy can replace that sympathetic discipline which is essential to any institution. The chaos, unhappiness and petty tyrannies that develop when good government is replaced by specious liberalization is seldom realized or believed by those who have not experienced it. Patients and staff have to comply with reasonable requests and restrictions.

During nurses' and attendants' meetings emphasis can be placed upon expanding patients' privileges until eventually patients have their own committee which participates in running the ward. At the same time, the reality principle that everyone has rights, including the attendant, can be emphasized. There is a tendency for some doctors to dominate such meetings by sitting together, thus emphasizing their status, or else by displaying their superior education. Some tend to make statements of opinion as though they are matters of fact. Other antithetical activity is unconsciously produced by people who talk too long, too polysyllabically or too vaguely, or who sidetrack important issues or resolutions of emotional conflicts. Charismatic attendants with radical political views have to be curbed from turning these meetings into a platform to preach political dogma. It is a mistake to regard these meetings as a democratic exercise. They are for reconnaissance, input and evaluation before the final briefing by the appropriate professional.

Education of all grades of nursing staff (Middleton, 1953) is important in producing a change of attitude. The recent training given to nurses and the knowledge required to pass the examination set by the General Nursing Council for their certificate for mental nursing did not necessarily qualify the nurse to treat mental patients. Indeed, a qualification can make people arrogant. Some medical students, when they qualify and are appointed to a job in their hospital, assume an air of authority and superiority to other students who may have been through university and hospital with them. This self-conscious prestige is called 'housemanitis' by medical students.

Sometimes an assistant nurse or inexperienced attendant is better in handling and organizing mentally sick people than the doubly trained fully qualified nurse. It is possible that too much attention is paid to the artificial external marks of merit and too little to ability. Training is desirable but, as I see it, often becomes little more than a fulfilment of a ritual that ceases when the examination is passed. Thus a caste system develops inimical to the therapeutic attitude. I do not think that examinations in mental nursing measure compassion and competency in understanding mentally ill people. Nevertheless, training and examinations are necessary if only to make students read their syllabus.

Regular visits to other hospitals are valuable if purposive. The nurse should go with a problem in mind and hope to find the solution in the hospital visited. Excursions on a rota system to hospitals not selected for any specific reasons are not usually educative. Non-specific visits, like desultory reading, tend to be a waste of time. After a visit it is helpful to have a discussion on what was seen and what is done better than at home. Ward discussions between attendants, nurses and the doctor on the principles of handling patients and the planning of the ward can help to create interest and enthusiasm. When parties of nurses first start going on such visits they tend to regard the excursion as a day off work and to adopt a frivolous attitude. When the novelty wears off, and others show interest in what they have seen and the suggestions they offer to improve practice in their own hospital, they benefit increasingly from such visits (Greenblatt et al., 1955).

Modified psychodrama, in which hospital personnel enact scenes that are meaningful in hospital life, encourages expression and is valuable in helping staff to gain insight. Members of the audience form a kind of jury and discuss what the nurse has done. Later the actors explain why they did what they did. This scrutiny of one's behaviour by others may be humiliating at times but does further self-understanding and awareness of the problems and difficulties of others.

In addition to the above principles more care needs to be taken to keep the head nurse and attendant happy at their job. The selection of mature personnel officers who will take a real interest in the hospital employees and their problems, personal and professional, together with the provision of adequate facilities for recreation, are obvious needs. There is something to be said for residential homes having a committee of attendants and nurses so that discontent has a forum for expression and does not smoulder under a superficial mask of obedience and acquiescence to regulations and orders in which the nurse has had no say.

In producing a sense of vocation in an attendant or a nurse, the charge nurses, the supervisors and the director of nursing are key figures. Their example and concern mould the attitude of those who work with them. Most people handle others badly when they start nursing. Prejudices, feelings of social inferiority, insecurity and lack of experience are often responsible. There are many exceptions. In starting a programme of rehabilitation and humanization it is vital to bring in senior staff first and not to disregard them in the implementation of the changes to be made.

The need for honesty with patients as well as with oneself is another important realization. Some employees tend to enter into agreements with relatives and tell white lies. When a relative has died they may feel the patient should not know and carry untrue reports to the patient about the relative's doings, afraid that the truth will cause further mental disorder.

Sometimes relatives have adopted the child of a patient, telling the child its parent is dead or pretending they are the parents. Under such circumstances great tact and diplomacy may be necessary to put the situation right. It is surprising how much patients understand and forgive such lies and the misguided motives responsible for them.

Apart from the harm which may be done by the various rituals demanded by administrative staff to demonstrate and maintain their superior status, the attitude of a doctor towards his work may be harmful to most of his patients. Some doctors are interested in individual psychotherapy which is very time-consuming. Because of this interest a doctor with 200 patients may devote 80 per cent of his time to perhaps half a dozen of his patients. The other 20 per cent of his time may be spent between the remaining 194 patients and routine demands such as yearly physical examinations, ward rounds, signing prescriptions on medicine cards, attending to anything the sister may bring to his notice, and writing letters. Thus 194 patients may be almost without medical attention.

Other doctors may find a case-load of 200 patients so overwhelming that they despair. Pratt (1948) wrote: 'A conversation illustrating this point took place at lunch at one hospital—a definitely inferior institution with manifold problems and a heavy patient load per physician. One of the younger doctors, recently arrived from a neurosis centre, unguardedly remarked that at the latter institution he had only had fifty patients in his charge, but he found that he had done much more work there than in his present position, where he was looking after over three hundred patients. This caused a general laugh, and offers of more work from his colleagues. He told me later that his time was largely taken up with the physical ills of his many charges, and the case-load, had he undertaken psychotherapy, would have been so overwhelming that he had given up hope of doing any significant psychiatry, and did only the bare minimum required of him.'

At one hospital the most junior doctor, often without psychiatric experience, was put in charge of 330 chronic patients and did also admissions, dental gases, an out-patient clinic, and looked after cases in the neurosis unit. No instruction in psychiatry was given but 'he could ask'. Sometimes a junior doctor may waste much of his time taking absurdly long histories or making long physical and mental examinations at the direction of the senior doctor for whom he is working. A doctor may not get much time to see his patients because he spends a long time with the charge nurse and attendants trying to alter their attitudes. Or they may demand his time because they are dissatisfied with their job and the life it entails. Some doctors are overconscientious and put in long hours, but there are a few who cling to the old mental hospital maxim 'half a day's work for half a day's pay'.

When applying for jobs doctors know that selection committees pay more attention to higher medical degrees and publications than to a sustained good work record. Furthermore, experience of treatments such as E.C.T., insulin, abreactions and psychotherapy is a more apparent and valuable asset than is sustained kindliness and probity with developing insight—which is so important in treating mental disorders in general and institutional neurosis in particular. Appointments committees cannot assess these dimensions of a candidate's psychiatric skill. Hard clinical work militates against publications.

The staffing of mental hospitals needs constant and careful scrutiny. The number of doctors and the methods of selection would seem to need investigation. Unless senior physicians are both aware of and actively concerned in preventing the factors which give rise to institutional neurosis it is likely to continue to arise. One potential method of combating the disorder would be to increase the medical staffing of mental hospitals. It is submitted that it is impossible for a conscientious doctor to look after 100 patients satisfactorily in hospital and provide adequate supervision to those discharged. Many psychiatrists realize this but feel powerless to do anything about it. An increase of staff is only potentially likely to counter institutional neurosis. To realize this potential, senior hospital staff must become aware of the disorder and its attendant causes, and be capable of helping to formulate and of executing plans to combat them.

Too often when psychologists, social workers and other para-medical employees are added to a hospital staff, instead of 'pitching in' and identifying and meeting unmet patient needs, they sit down in councils of war to decide what they themselves need and need not do. This may be the ultimate pattern in a nationalized, bureau-cratized, trade-unionized health service, but it is extremely expensive and job satisfaction far more difficult to achieve. It is a pity that work is ultimately organized as an outcome of the uneasy equilibrium between labour unions and management, administrative and clinical staff, and budgeting restriction and professional needs in such a manner that it is largely tedious and unrewarding as well as inefficient.

The attitude of staff is considerably influenced by the senior administration of a hospital. Administrations can wage war against clinical staff and vice versa. This fighting at hospital level is disastrous. It mops up the pep in its clinical programme, leaves no leeway to deal with emergencies and tends to sour senior administrators, slowly but surely, eroding the employees' sense of purpose so that patient care is subordinated to paper battles—and no matter which side wins the patient loses.

Obviously, decisions such as what is spent, what is to be done and who does what in the provision of services for the mentally ill are the final common factor deciding whether patients are abandoned or accepted, avoided or treated and how employees feel about their work. One essential requirement in running a psychiatric service is the delegation of effective executive authority—authority both for the officers directly responsible for running institutional and community mental health facilities and for the officers commissioned by the legislative body. If either attempts to usurp the authority of the other, neither can be truly effective. To be effective the authority delegated to an officer must allow him discretion—freedom from restraint— to deal with problems promptly as they arise. Checks and balances are essential but committees of management cannot become executive. As Macaulay said: 'Many an army has prospered under a bad General—but none under a debating society.'

Authoritarianism—the misuse of authority by an individual for his own personal satisfaction—has to be distinguished from authority. The nature of authority itself is complex. There are three main types: structural, sapiential and charismatic.

Structural authority is that endowed by an office or commission. For example, in an army, a captain is subordinated to a major, but superior to a lieutenant. A lieutenant's decisions prevail over a sergeant's and so forth—although in practice the matter as to whose view prevails in what circumstances is much more complicated than the principle illustrated. Out of office the office bearer loses his authority. In the American Declaration of Independence, governments are said to be 'deriving their just powers from the consent of the governed'. Government appointees in turn derive their authority from the government.

Sapiential authority is that derived from knowledge. The man who can usually get a television set or a motor car to work gains respect, and his views and recommendations are acted on rather than the suggestions of others. Qualifications should bring sapience— albeit they do not always do so, and should justifiably be doubted since certain pseudo-sciences are doing much harm in the world today. There is no substitute for the sapience of the well-trained professional in the provision of care and treatment of mentally ill people.

Charismatic authority depends neither on holding a position of authority nor having professional training and know-how. It is a certain primitive personal leadership which one finds in the demagogue and the stubborn industrial rebel.

In the most effective enterprises and with the most successful leaders all three types of authority—structural, sapiential and charismatic—are combined. The qualities necessary to run a good hospital, an efficient community service, a successful business enterprise, an effective educational establishment, a popular hotel, a happy ship, and so forth are very similar. They depend on the morale of employees, by which I mean *their willingness to help, readiness to seek out, identify and solve problems or meet needs*—which in, turn, depends on how these three forms of authority are curbed, supported, welded and applied.

Structural authority must be supported from above and it must be informed from below. Sapiential authority needs structure for its application or know-how will be diluted and lost in debate, discussion, consultation and the petulant clamour of competing claims. Charismatic authority has to be harnessed, curbed and directed or diverted. Its mobilization against structural and sapiential authority is subversive and destructive of purpose.

The realities of management are to be learned from the employees in the ward, appreciating their expectations and disappointments, their enthusiasms and indolences, their sensitivities and prejudices and their potential for compassion and cruelty. Each is individually different from another but with suitable encouragement and personal example most can develop kindness, professional competence and that paradoxical combination of humility and self-confidence which is the hallmark of the good professional.

The goodwill of employees is not a luxury, it is essential. It is not obtained by overcautious supervisory exercises with inquiries, inquisitions and retribution—when anything can be made to stick—as though the patterns of administration and discipline which worked with the Army and Navy 150 years ago (and even then uneasily and largely because backed up by severe stoppages of leave and pay, whippings and execution) could apply to professional staff in a psychiatric service today. A paramount fact that many administrators, committees and other people fail to learn is that kindness, pleasantness, sympathy and forbearance cannot be commanded by giving orders, writing guidelines or passing resolutions. These qualities can be found in 10–15 per cent of people regardless of the example they receive. For most people these qualities develop or fail to develop according to their respect for and the example of senior staff. Commanding these qualities is even more complicated than that; the nearest I can get to describing the background on which they flourish is 'morale' or 'team' spirit which arises from the way in which an institution is run, the way in which members of the staff are considered, recognized, praised, promoted, humiliated, disciplined or dismissed. For no institution of any size can run without rules and regulations and in running an institution fairness is more important than friendliness.

5. Encourage and make it possible for a Patient to have Friends, Possessions and to enjoy Personal Events

a. Friends

Initially the medical officer may stress to the relatives and friends of a patient the importance of maintaining visits, letters, outings and weekends at home. This could also be included in the hospital brochure.

Visits become less of an ordeal if the charge nurse, ward nurses and attendants welcome the visitor and regard him as a member of their team. I have found it useful to go round and sit down among the visitors and patients from time to time, talking to them. This conveys to visitors that they are noticed and necessary, and allows attendants to see how pleasant work becomes when one is friendly to patients and their visitors.

Many patients with a well-established institutional neurosis have few visitors. A psychiatric social worker, a charge nurse or a doctor can sometimes trace lost relatives who are often willing to join in a drive to reclaim the patient. The art of tracing relatives and enlisting their help is not easily acquired. Passively waiting for relatives to turn up is not enough. A positive drive needs to be made. Who should make the drive is often disputed. One system would be for the charge nurse or primary therapist to find out the names and addresses of relatives of patients who were not having regular visits. She would then inform the psychiatric social worker who could write and possibly call on the relatives. The doctor's role would be to manifest concern—always asking about visitors and asking the ward sister what relatives a patient had and why they did not come. The ward doctor could of course ask the psychiatric social worker directly but this would exclude nursing and attendant staff, thus diminishing their responsibility and dignity.

Patients without relatives may be visited by a member of the Hospital League of Friends or by ex-patients, some of whom, it will be found, like paying visits to the hospital and may be glad to take a patient under their wing.

The charge nurse, the psychiatric social worker and the doctor can help relatives and friends considerably in the early days of an illness by correcting misconceptions that lay people so often have about mental disorder. Relatives should be told the truth—preferably with the patient's permission. The possibility of dealing with relatives in groups has been tried and has proved successful (Ross, 1948). Possibly the doctor, psychiatric worker or charge nurse could meet relatives for this purpose for three-quarters of an hour before a ward party.

b. Possessions

Of enormous importance in the treatment of institutional neurosis is the provision of a place for the patient to keep personal possessions. A locker by the bed and a wardrobe for clothes are essential for each patient. Imagination is needed so that lockers and wardrobes enhance the dormitory's atmosphere, not detract from it. One gifted patient described new wardrobes as 'more like a row of coffins in an undertaker's'.

A combination wardrobe, chest of drawers, shelf and ward partition meets the requirements in a ward and adds privacy*. Since it is only 18 in (45·5 cm) wide and provides these facilities for 2 beds (i.e. only requires 9 in (23 cm) per bed) shortage of space cannot serve as an excuse for not making proper provision (*Fig.* 6).

Such equipment must harmonize with the colours of the ward and its furnishings. The widespread custom of leaving the choice of such items to a director of nursing or a supplies officer leaves the matter as a function of that individual's taste. It may be they will be discriminating and choose wisely, but it would seem better if more attention were given to such matters by specially skilled people. Many hospitals have 'follies' such as unsuitable wallpaper, clashing colours or inappropriate pictures with which patients have to live. An active secretary of a League of Friends could probably interest a professional interior decorator to help select and allocate furniture in conjunction with the charge nurse and nurses.

Although it is easier to give patients a brush and comb, bedroom slippers, soap, flannel, lipstick, and so on, the actual selection and purchase of such items by the patient herself is to be preferred, the nurse giving the minimum of assistance, yet sufficient to obtain the goods. Early excursions in shopping are best made to a hospital shop, and more venturous expeditions delayed until the patient has improved in order not to alienate local shopkeepers. Shopping at peak periods is best avoided until the very last days of the patient's stay in hospital. Photographs of relatives to stand on lockers are usually appreciated, and remind everybody that a patient is part of a human family and not an isolated case of mental illness. It may be objected that such knick-knacks would get lost or muddled up, but this happens less often if the patient has been helped to put her name on all her possessions and nurses are alerted to the importance of personal property and make inquiries when anything goes astray.

The effect of personal possessions is illustrated by Miss G. B., aged 57, who had not spoken for 23 years. She was moved to an open villa for rehabilitation, she began to speak, but went round to all the other lockers pilfering. (She had come from a ward which had no lockers.) A brush and comb were given to her with her name on together with other accessories. After a few weeks she stopped pilfering and began taking pride in her appearance and the care of her possessions. Similar experiences are common and well known to most hospital staff.

---

* Most manufacturers will be willing to make these if 100 or more are ordered. The price will be around £200 per unit, i.e. £100 per person.

Photo: Arthur Robinson

Fig. 6a.—Custom-built combination of a wardrobe, chest of drawers, shelf and mirror ward divider. Only 18 in (45·5 cm) wide, it provides the facilities for two people and allows patients a personal territory.

Photo: Jeffrey Burnard

Fig. 6b.—Wardrobe/ward dividers in use at Severalls Hospital, 1962.

c. Personal events

Personal events are those happenings more or less peculiar to the individual. In general hospitals patients take pride in standing birthday cards on their lockers, perhaps because it reassures them and tells others they are not alone in the world and they matter to someone else. An early project for a League of Friends could be to send an annual birthday card to patients without relatives and to arrange in cooperation with the charge nurse a birthday cake and tea in the ward to which relatives could be invited. Regular visiting, possibly using a rota system, makes landmarks in the patient's month which the primary therapist can make the patient aware of and encourage her to look forward to. A regular private talk with the charge nurse and doctor once a week also provides a fixed event of an individual nature and acts as an added landmark in the patient's week.

A patient cooking her own meals, having bought the raw materials, is more personal than the mass catering so widely practised. This may only be possible once or twice a week—but that is better than never.

If a household management unit is established it is important to use it morning, afternoon and evening—if possible 7 days a week. I have known such units used for group mornings only for 5 days a week, standing idle most of the time.

Other spontaneous personal events occur for example when a patient's knitting is admired, or when her relatives convey some family news to her, or relays a comment made by the nursing staff or doctor. It is important for every patient to be individually noticed in as many ways as possible.

Taking a coach load of fifty patients to the seaside or to a picnic is not so personal as when two or three make the journey by bus and train with a nurse. A journey with a nurse is not as personal as going with a relative.

Letting a patient choose her own clothes from a hospital shop provides her with a personal event, whereas to have to accept whatever a nurse doles out on a ward is impersonal. It is better still to go to a shop in a town and buy a garment than select one from a hospital shop. At different stages in the progress of rehabilitation each one of these methods may be the most appropriate.

In the prevention and treatment of institutional neurosis the difference between what is personal and impersonal *first needs to be realized* and then accent constantly placed on the personal.

6. Reduction of Drugs

The main difficulty in stopping drugs such as chlorpromazine, reserpine, barbiturates and paraldehyde is to persuade attendant and nursing staff that their continuous administration is not necessary for the large majority of patients. Everybody would agree that drugs should be used to counter the bewildering experiences and distressing emotions arising from within. Drugs should never be used to adjust a patient to surroundings or a regimen that any normal person would find intolerable. Withdrawal can be made suddenly in most cases but it is sometimes useful to prescribe a placebo in their place. Distranquillization, as soon as the principle is accepted, often produces gratifying results.

In March 1957 all sedatives were discontinued in Ward FA2 in Shenley Hospital. The number of draw-sheets sent to the laundry each day through urinary incontinence was significantly reduced and the nurses said the patients were easier to handle and to rouse in the morning. During April 1957 patients were given the same sedatives as before with a result that the number of draw-sheets soiled soon increased to the old numbers and nursing staff were incensed by the return to the old régime. When the drugs were again withdrawn in May 1957, the improvement noted in March re-appeared and persisted. Unfortunately the experiment was vitiated because the head nurse became too enthusiastic and began washing some of the draw-sheets in the ward.

A second attempt to assess the role of amylobarbitone sodium and chlorpromazine was made in Shenley Hospital in the first 3 months of 1958. In a geriatric unit of 200 patients 60 were found to be having a suspension of chlorpromazine 50 mg three times a day and tablets of amylobarbitone sodium 3 gr each night (Barton and Hurst, 1966).

For a period of 1 month dummy tablets dusted with quinine to make them bitter and white, suspension flavoured with ascorbic acid and quassia, were substituted. Five out of six ward sisters were unable to say in which month the substitution was made. The sixth gave the right month—she had been away from the ward for 2 weeks and on returning found her patients more disturbed. However, she stated this always happened after she had been away. This is a matter which needs investigation, and when investigations are reported it should be remembered that the attitude of the investigator is all important to the results obtained (Clark, 1956; Feldman, 1956; Leveton, 1958; Eisen et al., 1959).

That drugs have unexpected side-effects on attitude and clinical judgement has been noted (Barton, 1963).

Rees (1957) makes a pointed and witty reference to the possible uselessness of tranquillizers. My experience, on the whole, supports his scepticism. It is a pity that we are all so gullible. It was ever thus. Bacon, who introduced scientific methods and stressed the importance of observations as a basis of knowledge, wrote in his essay *Of Friendship*: 'You may take Sarza to open the ear, steel to open the spleen, flower of sulphur for the lungs and castoreum for the brain.'

Berkeley, whose aim was 'to liberate men's minds from confusion and fundamental mistakes', seems to have believed and propagated the exaggerated medicinal claims of tar water. Lucretius (98–55 B.C.) in *De Rerum Natura* tried to free men from superstition and inherited beliefs by making them understand the universe. A sadder reflection is the fact that whereas the money spent on research into mental disorders is niggardly and the salaries for research workers parsimonious and tied up by complicated bureaucratic and committee procedures, the money for advertizing tranquillizing drugs is plentiful and comparatively freely available.

It would be foolish to say that all patients should be without drugs, but it seems likely that many are better without them. When a patient is not sleeping, a warm drink and a small snack, especially if patients are encouraged wherever possible to get it for themselves in the ward kitchen, may be more effective than a medicine glass of paraldehyde. When the acute phase of a psychosis has passed, occupation and reaction may be more effective than tranquillizing drugs. Whatever evidence is produced to support the effect of tranquillizers, Brown and Connolly in England, and Todd, Woodward and Butler in America (Bockoven, 1956), and others produced remarkable results long before tranquillizers were known, and when general paralysis of the insane, an incurable disease, was a common cause of admission to asylums, as psychiatric hospitals were then called. In a few cases tranquillizers do seem effective. Too often they get the credit for the effect produced by the enthusiasm and dedication of staff that goes with them and the other measures adopted. Too often they are substituted for 'moral treatment'.

7. Provision of a Homely, Friendly, Permissive Ward Atmosphere

The general impression a ward creates is important because it is continuously communicating to the patient whether she matters and whether her behaviour matters. Drab surroundings with dingy furniture, locked doors and barred windows do not encourage a patient to feel that life can be interesting or that effort is worth while. Thus it is helpful in treating institutional neurosis to pay attention to everything that can be perceived in a ward. Brightly coloured carpets, cushions, curtains and other soft furnishings can create an air of optimism which is a valuable contributory factor to other measures of rehabilitation. Walls are best painted off-white. They then glow with colours from the curtains and reflected colours from the furnishings. Plenty of pictures hung at eye level are necessary to prevent a sterile white look.

Nursing-staff morale seems to improve when a ward is redecorated and so does the patients' behaviour. The amount of tearing and smashing drops. There is, however, the possibility that this is brought about by other changes usually occurring at the same time. The effect of redecoration and refurnishing alone has not been determined. It seems reasonable to believe that it plays a large part. There is a need in many mental hospitals for greater coordination and discrimination in redecorating and refurnishing. Perhaps the most satisfactory method would be for the charge nurse, nurses, patients and ward doctor to draw up a plan and submit it to an expert for modification and approval. The fact that a psychiatrist, hospital secretary, supplies officer or senior nurse is qualified for their special job does not mean they are qualified in making aesthetic judgements or gifted with the imagination necessary to plan and effect a pleasing ward. Garishly coloured or drab walls destroy the ambience of brightness and optimism that is so desirable.

Similarly the choice of pictures needs care and skill. Hanging the paintings by patients in wards where they live, on the grounds that 'it is impossible to judge a work of art', is bad practice. Some patients produce pleasing pictures, but many are ugly and unpleasant and their use as decoration conveys the impression 'anything is good enough'. The guiding principle is to communicate to the patient, 'You matter'. If the patient has a say in the selection of the pictures hanging in her ward this message will be more personal. To enable this choosing, a picture library should be arranged in a hall or a corridor. A hundred or so pictures should be well arranged and lighted. Once a month a group of four to six patients can return ten pictures from the ward and select ten others from the gallery to go in their place. Pictures need regular dusting and cleaning. Uniformity of sizes as far as possible enables areas of non-faded wall to be covered by the new picture. The expedition occasions an interesting and therefore useful exercise for the patients concerned. The goal of selecting replacement for the returned pictures promotes interaction between patients and staff. *The possibility of rehabilitation springs from amiable, concerned helpfulness of staff in carrying out some purposive activity.*

The activity and appearance of patients also affect ward atmosphere. Participation in a ward programme improves behaviour generally and this improvement is furthered by kindly criticism. The appearance of patients, on the other hand, may remain poor unless a specific drive is made first to improve things with the patient remaining passive. The nurse or hairdresser can shampoo and set the patient's hair. Prescribing a pint of shampoo to do the hair of a whole ward from the hospital dispensary which costs about 20p possibly has a greater tranquillizing effect than prescribing chlorpromazine for one person for a week at 40p. Superfluous hair on the face can be removed with an electric razor. It is a fallacy that this makes the hair grow stronger. Powder, lipstick and other cosmetics can be applied. Similarly the standard of clothes and shoes can be raised. Brassières and corsets are important to the appearance of many women, yet some mental hospitals do not stock them.

The second step is gradually to get the patients to make efforts as well as the nurses, to persuade and encourage them to take care of their appearance without help. Some patients will join in if they see the nurses making up on the ward. Imitation is important in the early stages of activation. Patients can sometimes be persuaded to do each other's hair if they are given the chance and eventually some will be able to manage completely without help. To devote two hours to clothes, dressing and beauty culture immediately before a ward party to which men have been invited adds zest to these activities. Similarly it has been found that if male patients know they are going to mix with women they are more willing to shave, dress carefully and polish their shoes. Obviously it is not enough to get patients all dressed up and give them nowhere to go and nothing to do. A good standard should be expected on the ward, and always, before going out, patients should spend a little time on their shoes, stockings, face and hair in order to realize the importance that outside people attach to general appearance. A full-length mirror is necessary in every dormitory. It does not hurt patients to see themselves as others see them. Although the nurse and the doctor may tire of telling patients that they look nice, that their clothes are pleasing, and so on, the fact that they show interest has an effect on the patient who begins to be concerned about herself. For example, Mrs K., aged 36 years, had been in hospital for 7 years. She had become incontinent and careless of her appearance. For most of the day she sat dribbling and spitting, hunched up in a chair. Intensive doses of reserpine administered over some weeks had little effect. When she was given new clothes, moved to another ward, and the head nurse and attendants began showing increased concern about her she improved and lost all her unpleasant habits. I last saw her 2 years later when I signed photographs for a passport for her to go on a holiday to Italy. It may be objected that doctors, nurses and visitors communicate their attitude to the patient's appearance without words. Verbal expression of concern is the most important in treating institutional neurosis, since the non-verbal language of gesture, expressions and posture is often ignored or misinterpreted by patients.

In most wards of a mental hospital smell is no problem. Where there is urinary incontinence the problem may arise. It can be tackled in several ways. First, the incidence of incontinence falls if drugs are decreased. Regular excursions to the lavatory decrease it still more. Second, the use of waterproof materials without cracks or crevices on sofas, chairs and floors prevents urea accumulating and being broken down to ammoniacal compounds which produce the smell. In one ward for incontinent patients with senile dementia the smell that had been present for many years was finally 'exorcised' by sanding and sealing the floor and laying down a light grey polyvinyl floor-covering. The light colour, unpopular with some members of the staff, had to be cleaned regularly and frequently, but the odour of urine disappeared. Furniture covered with plastic can look attractive but the backs and arms should not reach the seats. Third, the possibility of blowing warmed air into a room deserves attention since it blows out the smell. Draughts due to open windows clear localized parts of a ward but other parts may remain stagnant. The use of deodorants is wasteful. They have no effect on clearing the smell from a ward. They act by suggestion and although providing an alternative smell may convince staff, who have faith in them, there is no smell, it is often all too apparent to the visitor who has not seen the deodorant or does not share their faith. The characteristic smell of mental hospital wards common until the 1960's was a combination of decomposing urine, paraldehyde which is excreted in the lungs and cheap shag tobacco.

Noise is a feature of ward life to which hospital employees tend to become inured. Noises made by the staff are usefully considered separately from those made by patients.

The clatter of pulling screens too energetically, moving commodes, slamming and locking doors, walking about the ward with noisy shoes, banging into beds are some examples of a possible non-verbal communication to the patients that they do not matter. The rattle of keys is a constant reminder of imprisonment and the hopelessness of effort. One of the worst sources of 'staff noise' is the ritual of rounds during the patients' sleeping hours. Many patients complain of being awakened by the noisy sound of a key fumbling in a lock followed by a click, a clatter and the noise of a night officer making her rounds. Insomnia in an institution is not so much a result of illness as a result of the institution. Many people are never able to 'sleep through anything'. The reduction of night rounds to a minimum or their abolition would reduce this source of noise. Also it would save a lot of unnecessary ritual that seems to be carried out more for the protection of staff in the case of any untoward event rather than for patients' welfare. Employees have a dread they will be in trouble if a patient is found dead in bed in the morning. It would be a foolish coroner who would criticize a night nurse for not knowing a patient had died in her sleep.

Clattering delivery of milk cans or food containers in the early morning often awakens people who cannot get off to sleep again. A ringing telephone is another frequent source of complaint. Sometimes it is a wrong number that awakens several patients. It would be neither difficult nor expensive to install a flashing dull red signal, screened to avoid direct light falling on sleeping patients and yet visible to the night nurse.*

Similarly attention needs to be paid to doors so that answering the telephone does not start up another sequence of noise. Strips of carpet in wards, balloon tyres on trolley wheels which are kept well oiled, and, perhaps most important, *manifest concern* on the part of directors and head nurses about noise are other requirements to reduce noise arising from staff activities.

This concern must be backed up by business and supplies officers so that the necessary equipment is forthcoming. They in turn require support and encouragement and understanding from auditors. Incalculable harm has been done by centralizing supplies and allowing them to be controlled by obsessive, unimaginative officers with a contempt for the recommendations made by professional staff. Some sounds are pleasing and add to the friendly peaceful atmosphere of a ward. The sound of people talking, birdsong and noises which occur because the nurses feel cheerful rather than that they are in a hurry or ill-tempered are examples of pleasing sounds.

Other noises come from patients. Shouting is one of the more difficult to cope with and is not always stopped by giving sedatives—unless an anaesthetic dose is used. It is surprising how the amount of shouting dies in a ward where patients realize they matter and the staff is with them. Occasionally a very demented patient may be noisy, especially at night when confusion due to brain damage turns the unfamiliar shadows of the surroundings into an illusory population of persecutors. Such noisy patients often quieten down and sleep if put in a side-room with the light on all night. Many respond to reassurance, but occasionally a soundproofed room, with transparent swing doors, would prevent other patients being disturbed. Snorers and people with asthmatic attacks can with advantage sleep apart from the communal dormitory. If a patient requires a lot of nursing or medical attention he can sleep in a side-room so that the noise of apparatus working and the bustle of staff will not disturb the rest. Similarly a patient who is about to die can be discreetly moved to a side-room to save the rest of the ward distress.

There is a serious drawback to having good interior decorating, furnishing and well-dressed patients. It presents a superficially good impression to members of management committees and other visitors. Thus a hospital or ward may be given a report in glowing

---

* Since first writing these passages about noise a Ministry of Health memorandum, H.M. (61)68, which makes many useful suggestions, has been published.

terms when, in fact, it may be causing institutional neurosis because the other seven factors obtain.

In assessing a mental hospital the looks of the ward should never get more than 13 per cent of the total marks. The other seven factors should be rated equally important and awarded a possible total of 13 per cent each. Questions that need to be asked of the head nurses, attendants and patients, preferably with the agreement of the hospital official showing the person round, for militant fault finding becomes self-defeating, are:

a. What do you do to keep patients in contact with their homes and relations? How often are they visited? How often does she or he go home for the weekend? For holidays? How far is their home? How much does it cost to travel there and back?

b. How are patients occupied? Are they being trained in new work or are old skills being rehabilitated to enable them to return to the community?

c. Do you have many bruises and fractures on this ward? Who looks into the cause? Are patients ever ill-treated, do you suppose? What happens if an employee hits a patient? Who would report it and to whom? (If a patient with a bruise is encountered do not hold an on-the-spot inquisition. Find out the patient's name and let the doctor and director of nursing know—*see* page 47.)

d. What rules and regulations have you? Who makes them? How are they enforced?

e. What attention is paid to the personal lives of the patients— have they private possessions, friends, etc.? (Never trust anyone who says: 'They are too bad, or too mad, or too far gone to appreciate such things.' It is very rarely true.)

f. How many patients are having sleeping tablets? Sedatives? Tranquillizers? How many have nothing?

g. What prospects are there for patients of going home and getting work outside? How do you let them know such prospects exist?

It is important that members of management committees and visiting doctors should ask the charge nurse, ward doctor, nurses, attendants and patients these questions. Manifestation of concern about such things is never wasted. It does more good than giving orders, but, unlike orders, it cannot be repeated too often.

8. Make the Patient aware of Prospects of Accommodation, Work and Friends outside Hospital

a. Accommodation

Accommodation is a source of worry and frustration to patients. If arrangements can be made and the patient told he or she becomes less afraid of leaving hospital. Relatives can be sounded when a good relationship has been established. There are many who are unable or unwilling to accommodate an ex-mental patient. There are many patients without relatives.

Patients who have full-time jobs outside hospital, but are living in, can sometimes be successfully accommodated in lodgings. A League of Friends and psychiatric social workers in conjunction with the mental welfare officers and district nurses might be able to make a register of suitable landladies. Ex-patients will sometimes be able to provide accommodation. Wherever possible, some attempt at matching the patient to the relative or landlady should be made, to achieve as good conditions as possible. Brown et al. (1958) have found evidence that suggests that schizophrenics are best not sent back to live with their parents.

Sometimes accommodation goes with the job. Before leaving hospital, if an accommodation difficulty is known, a patient may be given practice in the kind of work which carries accommodation with it. For an example, some hospitals and firms have hostels for their employees.

Hostels provide accommodation but usually it is difficult to secure a place, and to some the thought of living in a strange community is worse than remaining secure in hospital. It is generally advocated that much more needs to be done in providing local hostels for discharged patients. Some local authorities are willing to cooperate but are handicapped because the mental hospital has no agreed plan. Few residents' associations are agreeable to having a hostel in their neighbourhood. The way in which hostels are managed and staffed gives rise to some concern. Mentally trained and qualified attendants and nurses need constant assistance from senior nursing staff and doctors to run their wards therapeutically rather than custodially. The same degree of support and supervision cannot be given the warden of a hostel and although exceptional personalities may carry out the task satisfactorily, others may lapse into the errors of mental hospitals of the past. Probably supervised lodgings and subsidized housing are greater needs than hostels.

It would seem possible to make one building serve three purposes: (1) A hostel to act as a transition stage between living in the hospital and living independently. (2) A day hospital to treat patients without bringing them into hospital, and a geriatric day club. (3) A social club to serve as the headquarters of the League of Friends and provide evening social events for ex-patients and their friends and relations.

If housing ever gets easier it will probably be possible to discharge patients in pairs to live in flats or council houses. For example, Mrs E. T., aged 47 years, was admitted to hospital some years ago with schizophrenia. A leucotomy had little effect on her. With a liberal régime she improved sufficiently to make a friend and work outside hospital. Eventually she and her friend bought a caravan and have since lived successfully and independently from hospital.

Purchase of houses by Leagues of Friends, etc., and allocation of council houses by local authorities are other solutions to the problem of accommodation. It is important to realize that a wide range of different facilities is desirable—a mosaic of services—so that the individual needs of a patient can be best met.

Whatever accommodation a patient gets, regular visits from her charge nurse, nurse and psychiatric social worker are helpful and visits to psychiatric out-patients essential. Assistance with rent, neighbours and landlords may be necessary. Such intervention should be kept minimal but enough to keep the person out of hospital. It is essential that the patient be encouraged to find her own solutions whenever possible.

b. Work

The first stage in the cure of institutional neurosis is to get the patient active in any way to which he or she seems to respond.

The next stage is work in the hospital aimed at re-establishing the pattern of work present before admission. The patient should not be sent to a department and forgotten. The doctor, the head nurse, the primary therapist, the hospital employment officers, the psychiatric social worker and the head of the department must focus attention on the patient and their ultimate target, a job in the community. In many cases the most that can be done is to reclaim old skills such as shorthand and typing, laundry or domestic work. Much more therapeutic use of shops, the cinema, the canteen, wards and laundry could be made in most hospitals. Some patients could be trained to become waitresses, shop assistants, usherettes and so on. Work done in hospital needs always to be directed at the community. Hospital training schemes need to be adapted towards the kind of work available in the patients' catchment area. Industrial therapy is important providing that it re-establishes the habit of getting up and getting to work on time, of discharging responsibility for a task, and of accepting the kind of discipline that will be met at work outside hospital. Liaison between job centres, employment agencies, local firms and most hospitals needs to be increased. Patients may be able to work locally and live in the hospital for a time.

Before any patient applies for a job outside hospital she should be 'coached' to improve her chances. She should go to the hairdresser; her clothes should be scrutinized in every detail. Cosmetics should by this time be a habit and any tendencies to excess, bizarre or unfashionable make-up should have been corrected. For example,

Mrs C. K., aged 45 years, had sat shouting in a ward for many years. People heard her at times over a hundred yards from the ward. She wrote copious notes on the wall of her side-room and had ideas of sexual interference through television. She responded amazingly well to an intensive course of reserpine and liberalizing measures. When she went for an interview for the first job she applied for, her hair was sticking out, she had an excess of rouge on her cheeks and her clothes clashed in a bizarre fashion. She was unsuccessful. Subsequently with training and contact with her home her dress sense improved, she began using cosmetics in a fashionable way, went to a hairdresser, and successfully competed with normal people for a job which she held for some years.

A mock interview can help the potential worker. A nurse, a volunteer or another patient takes the role of the prospective employer. Other patients at a similar stage provide an audience. The prospective employer asks questions. Thus the patients get practice in dealing with a difficult situation and collectively arrive at answers to questions that too often floor them.

Some firms are very cooperative in the employment of patients, but liaison between the firms' welfare officers and the psychiatric social worker may help to iron out some difficulties and avoid others.

Putting notices on the ward notice-board and letters from patients who have left and are successfully working can help patients to realize work is a possibility and preferable to hospital life.

The importance of regular occupation has been known for many years. Galen wrote in A.D. 172: 'Employment is nature's best physician and is essential to human happiness.' Tuke, Connolly, and Brown put forward similar ideas over 100 years ago and Bleuler (1905) and Jaspers (1913) emphasized the importance of regular occupation. Bleuler 'trained his nurses and attendants to supervise the patients' activities so that they gave him satisfaction and, if possible, some personal responsibility' (Mayer-Gross et al., 1954).

The value of doing socially useful work in preparing to make a patient capable and ready for life outside hospital is remarked on by Jones et al. (1956), an objective albeit not always reached. The enormous difference between filling in a patient's time with handicrafts and encouraging him to work purposively has been brought out again and again (Jones et al., 1956; May 1956). A medical research unit established a factory at Banstead Hospital which was reported on by Baker (1956), and O'Connor and Rawnsley (1959). It was found that regular work by patients resulted in considerable increase of production but no measurable change in social behaviour could be recorded. Wadsworth et al. (1958) have given their experience and suggestions in running an industrial unit in a mental hospital. Shoenberg and Morgan (1958) gave an excellent description of the role played by work in a schizophrenic unit they formed. The great problem is that these schemes are often doctor-centred and once the enthusiast goes the scheme folds up. The need to make such schemes independent of any one person and self-propagating requires a great deal of attention. Perhaps the pattern described by Early (1960) of an industrial therapy organization at Bristol has greater chance of permanence.

The importance of money as an incentive was brought home to me soon after taking up appointment as physician superintendent of Severalls Hospital in 1960. A patient was encouraged to take a job in Colchester. At the end of the week he received a wage packet with £7* in notes. The following Monday 6 or 7 patients called on me to ask if they might be allowed to earn 'real' money.

It is perhaps relevant to quote Viteles (1932) on motives in industry: 'The ways in which workers are hired, trained, paid, promoted, disciplined and dismissed are important determiners of attitude. Curt treatment by superiors, monotonous meaningless work, lack of opportunity for self-development, excessive fatigues, the unreasonable use of punishment will be deeply felt. Such factors mould attitudes, constitute the sources of motives and produce the ineffective unfit worker and the average industrial rebel.' The same principles apply to work in the mental hospital.

c. Loneliness

This is a great problem for many patients discharged from hospital. Making new friends is not easy. Hospital staff have not the time to combat loneliness directly but they can do a lot through organization and cooperation with local authorities. A social club is very necessary if a hospital is to fit into its catchment area. Patients should be encouraged to attend this club before they leave hospital so that they accept it as part of their way of life.

Churches often have organizations that patients can attend in the evenings and sometimes patients can be persuaded to attend evening classes. Subsidiary groups of people can sometimes be organized into doing something together. For an example, while in hospital they could be taught to paint with oils. After discharge the patients could be asked to attend out-patients on the same afternoon and eventually be persuaded to hold weekly painting sessions in each other's homes in rotation.

The League of Friends can play a very important role in preventing loneliness. Mental welfare officers, psychiatric social workers and

---

* The average wage in England at that time was £12 a week. I was earning £40 a week.

ex-patients can pay visits to a patient in her own home. An occasional visit of nurses from the hospital is also desirable, but again the problem of transport and organization needs to be solved. An active hospital car service or a few motor-scooters with requisite driving instruction available to nurses might contribute greatly by mobilizing nursing staff and emphasizing the importance of such visits.

The possibility of selected discharged patients being asked by local authorities to help with visiting old-age pensioners and other lonely people is worth examining. Coordination and liaison through local mental welfare officers and social workers could possibly be effected through the social club. Trustworthy patients could be given the names and addresses of old people to visit. Having purposeful activity useful to other people gives a sense of social dignity. This is one of the best antidotes to loneliness.

Chapter 5

Wider Implications of Institutional Neurosis

Although identified in psychiatric hospitals, institutional neurosis may occur anywhere where a large number of people live, work, eat, sleep and play under the supervision of a small number of staff in crowded places. Orphanages, boarding schools, monasteries, ships, barracks, prisons, prisoner-of-war camps and homes for the aged, indigent or blind are examples. It is the all-enveloping tissue of constraints and lack of privacy which mainly distinguishes such a population from a normal village or town. The difference is essentially one of quantity rather than quality. Submission to the rule of law and disposition to lead a more or less ordered life are essential for most members of a society to enable other members to lead a civilized existence. Everyone has to accept some abridgement of his freedoms, some restrictions of his actions if the relative freedom of others is to be preserved. Normal maturation is the process of learning to deny, divert or delay impulses and gratifications according to the prescription of society. It is extremeness of submission and failure to recognize the potential of life beyond the institution that is pathological.

The term 'institution' should not be restricted to denote collections of buildings which house organizations such as schools or mental hospitals. 'Institution' embraces non-tangible innovations such as marriage, religion, benevolence, due process, justice, customs and mores and so forth. Some of these innovations have evolved with the mental and physical evolution of the human species. Others have been instituted suddenly by administrative fiat. From time to time charismatic leaders have made institutions—Alfred the Great divided England into counties and hundreds, founded Oxford University and collected, compiled and established the best enactments of his predecessors to institute a legal system. Others have broken them—Adolf Hitler and Stalin destroyed and dissipated their peoples' slowly accumulated treasures of benevolence, reason and justice.

Institutional neurosis occurs when the original purposes of an institution are ignored, displaced by or subordinated to increasing preoccupation with the rituals or symbols of administration or wealth of that institution. The mechanical chanting of prayers while appraising a fellow worshipper, rigid adherence to the letter at the expense of the spirit of the law, investment of time and personnel in otiose administrative exercises and paper work in health services and hospitals with disregard and neglect of the patients' treatment, comfort or feelings are examples of neurotic distortions of institutions in which the institution itself has become valued above the purpose it was founded to serve.

It becomes apparent that, far from being a rejection of reality, institutional neurosis represents an adjustment to an institution the purpose of which is not fully understood or transacted by its executive. The examples given of abnormal submission, meaningless prayers or legalistic rituals may be aspects of a personal or social neurosis in the individual. The antics of legislative, administrative or professional staff obscuring and perverting the primary purpose of the institution to self-serving is analogous to a psychosis: its transactions failing to identify or heed the realities of its purpose, and consuming its resources in activities irrelevant—and sometimes harmful—to the very objectives for which it was founded.

Summary

Institutional Neurosis

This is a disease characterized by apathy, lack of initiative, loss of interest, especially in things of an impersonal nature, submissiveness, apparent inability to make plans for the future, lack of individuality, and sometimes a characteristic posture and gait.

Differential Diagnosis

It is only recently that these symptoms have been recognized as a disorder separate from the one which brought the patient into hospital. They may coexist with features of schizophrenia such as delusions or hallucinations. Distinction from the later stages of schizophrenia can sometimes only be made by observing the response to treatment. Depression has symptoms in common, but in institutional neurosis the gloominess, sadness and guilt are absent. Organic dementias may be complicated by the disorder so that rehabilitation is necessary to decide which symptoms are attributable to what. Myxoedema may be recognized by the face, falling hair, croaking voice, constipation and raised serum cholesterol. The posture and gait have to be distinguished from that of Parkinsonism, especially Parkinsonism due to reserpine and chlorpromazine.

Thus, after 2 years in mental hospitals most patients are suffering from two illnesses: (1) Schizophrenia; (2) Institutional neurosis.

Name

Institutional neurosis should be considered a disease in its own right because:

1. It occurs in institutions whether mental hospitals or otherwise, e.g. prisoner-of-war camps, orphanages, prisons, tuberculosis sanatoria, displaced persons camps.

2. It seems unlikely that mental disorders, regardless of their type, produce an end state similar to institutional neurosis.

3. Rehabilitation resolves these symptoms in many, not all, patients.

4. Hospitals run by a staff aware of the neurosis are ceasing to produce it.

5. A schizophrenic whose relations are prepared and can afford to look after him in his own home does not deteriorate or regress

to the same extent as one neglected in a large back ward of a mental hospital.

Aetiology

Uncertain. The probably causes of the illness are:

1. Loss of contact with the outside world.
2. Enforced idleness and loss of responsibility.
3. Brutality, browbeating and teasing.
4. Bossiness of professional staff.
5. Loss of personal friends, possessions and personal events.
6. Drugs.
7. Ward atmosphere.
8. Loss of prospects outside the institution.

Prognosis

Although the schizophrenic episode or depression may clear up, the institutional neurosis will persist as long as the patient remains in hospital and the hospital remains unchanged. (Exceptions often occur.)

Treatment

1. Re-establish contacts with the family and community in every possible way.

2. Make patients active and gradually establish a sequence of events 14 hours a day, 7 days a week, bearing in mind that regimentation and organization from above, necessary in the early stages of treatment, perpetuate the disease in the later stages.

3. Eradicate brutality, browbeating and teasing.

4. Alter attitudes of hospital employees (if necessary). This cannot be done by giving orders and is not usually achieved by psychoanalysis.

5. Encourage friends, provide for possessions and assist in bringing about personal events, i.e. the patient must be 'in the swim'.

6. Reduce drugs and distranquillize where possible.

7. Produce a friendly, homely, permissive ward atmosphere. Each patient needs a wardrobe, chest of drawers, shelf and chair by her or his bed.

8. Make the patient aware of prospects of accommodation, work and friends outside hospital and assist him or her in realizing these prospects.

References

Asher R. A. (1947) *Br. Med. J.* **2**, 967.
*Baker, A. A. (1956) *Lancet* **1**, 278.
Barrett J. (1948) *Am. J. Psychiatry* **105**, 379.
Barton R. (1963) *Ment. Hosps* **14**, 654.
Barton R., Elkes A. and Glen F. (1961) *Lancet* **1**, 1220.
Barton R. and Hurst L. (1966) *Br. J. Psychiatry* **112**, 989.
Bell G. M. (1955) *Int. J. Soc. Psychiatry* **1**, 42.
Bennet D. H. (1955) *J. Ment. Sci.* **101**, 664.
Bettelheim B. and Sylvester E. (1948) *Am. J. Orthopsychiatry* **18**, 191.
*Bickford J. A. R. (1955) *Lancet* **2**, 917, 969.
Bleuler E. (1905) *Psychiat.-neurol. Wschr.* **6**, 441. (Quoted by Mayer-Gross and others.)
Bockoven J. S. (1956) *J. Nerv. Ment. Dis.* **124**, 175, 194, 319.
Brooks G. W., Chittick R. A., Irons F. S. and Deane W. N. (1961) *The Vermont Story.* Published at Vermont State Hospital, Waterbury, Vt.
Brown G. W. (1959) *Br. Med. J.* **2**, 1300.
Brown G. W., Carstairs G. M. and Topping G. (1958) *Lancet* **2**, 685.
Brown W. A. F. (1854) In: Easterbrook C. E. (1940) *The Chronicle of Crichton Royal.* Dumfries.
*Brown W. A. F. (1856) Quoted by Hunter R. (1956) *Lancet* **1**, 98.
Butler J. S. (1887) *Curability of Insanity and the Individualized Treatment of the Insane.* New York, G. P. Putnam's Sons. (Quoted by Bockoven J. S. (1956).)
*Cameron J. L., Laing A. D. and McGhie A. (1955) *Lancet* **2**, 1384.
Carse J., Panton N. and Watt A. (1958) *Lancet* **1**, 39.
*Carstairs G. M., Clark D. H. and O'Connor N. (1955) *Lancet* **2**, 1025.
Clark D. H. (1958) *Lancet* **1**, 805.
Clark L. D. (1956) *Dis. Nerv. Syst.* **17**, 282.
Connolly J. J. (1856) *The Treatment of the Insane without Mechanical Restraints.* London, Smith, Elder & Co.
Cumming J. and Cumming E. (1962) *Ego and Milieu.* London, Tavistock. (Contains many useful references to contributions by American workers.)
Early D. F. (1960) *Lancet* **2**, 754.
Eisen S. B., Sabshin M. and Heath M. (1959) *J. Nerv. Ment. Dis.* **128**, 256.
Epicharmus, quoted by Osler W. (1906) British Medicine in Greater Britain. In: *Aequanimitas, with Other Addresses.* London, Lewis.
Feldman P. E. (1956) *Am. J. Psychiatry* **113**, 52.
Freudenberg R. K., Bennet D. H. and May A. R. (1957) *Congr. Int. Psychiatry* **1**, 157.
Goffman E. (1961) *Asylums.* New York, Anchor Books, Doubleday.
Goncharov I. A. (1858) *Oblomov.* Everyman's Library 878. London, Dent, p. 58.
Greenblatt M., York R. and Brown E. (1955) *From Custodial to Therapeutic Patient Care in Mental Hospitals.* New York, Russell Sage Foundation.
Gruenberg E. M. (1962) *Mental Disorders: A Guide to Control Methods.* New York, American Public Health Association.
Henry J. (1954) *Psychiatry* **17**, 129.

REFERENCES

*Hunter R. (1956) *Lancet* **1**, 98.
Jaspers K. (1913) *Allgemeine Psychopathologie.* (14th ed. (1948), p. 700.) Berlin.
Jones K. (1972) *History of the Mental Health Services.* London, Routledge & Kegan Paul.
*Jones M., Pomryn B. A. and Skellern E. (1956) *Lancet* **1**, 543.
Leveton A. F. (1958) *Am. J. Pyschiatry* **115**, 232.
MacMillan D. (1958) *Lancet* **2**, 201.
Marshall B. (1952) *The White Rabbit.* London, Evans.
*Martin D. (1955) *Lancet* **2**, 1188.
*May A. R. (1956) *Lancet* **1**, 500.
Mayer-Gross W., Slater E. and Roth M. (1954) *Clinical Psychiatry.* London, Cassell, p. 281.
Middleton J. (1953) *Am. J. Psychiatry* **110**, 113.
Myerson A. (1939) *Am. J. Psychiatry* **95**, 1197.
O'Connor N. and Rawnsley K. (1959) *Br. J. Med. Psychol.* **32**, 142.
Pratt D. (1948) *Public Mental Hospitals in England: A Survey.* U.S.A., National Mental Health Foundation Inc.
Pugh D. L. (1955) *Lancet* **1**, 614.
Rees T. P. (1957) *J. Ment. Sci.* **103**, 309.
Report on Motivation (1964) Published by Mental Hospital Service of the American Psychiatric Association (Smith, Kline & French Foundation), Box 7929, Philadelphia 1, Pa.
Robb B. (1967) *Sans Everything.* London, Nelson.
Roland P. (1948) *Am. J. Psychiatry* **105**, 353.
Ross W. D. (1948) *Am. J. Psychiatry* **104**, 623, 13.
Shalit P. (1948) *Am. J. Psychiatry* **105**, 379.
Shoenberg E. and Morgan R. (1958) *Lancet* **2**, 412.
Stanton A. H. and Schwartz M. S. (1954) *The Mental Hospital. A Study of Institutional Participation in Psychiatric Illness and Treatment.* London, Tavistock.
Sydenham T., quoted by Osler W. (1906) British Medicine in Greater Britain. In: *Aequanimitas, with Other Addresses.* London, Lewis.
Vail D. J. (1966) *Dehumanization and the Institutional Career.* Springfield, Thomas.
Viteles M. S. (1932) *Industrial Psychology.* New York, Norton, p. 585.
Wadsworth W. V., Scott R. F. and Tonge W. L. (1958) *Lancet* **2**, 896.
Wallace A. F. C. (1967) Anthropology and Psychiatry. In: Freedman A. M. and Kaplan H. I. (ed.), *Comprehensive Textbook of Psychiatry.* Baltimore, Williams & Wilkins, p. 199.
Wing J. K. (1962) *Br. J. Soc. Clin. Psychol.* **1**, 38.

* Articles marked with an asterisk were published in the booklet entitled *In the Mental Hospital,* published by *The Lancet* in 1957.

Index

Accommodation outside hospital,
  gradual move of patient into, 41
— — — making the patient aware of
  prospects of, 68–70
— — — need for wide range of
  types, 70
— — — severe difficulties in
  finding, 20
Administrative staff (*see* Hospital
  administrators)
Aetiology or factors associated with
  institutional neurosis, 6–7, 26
— summary of, 77
Aggressive episodes in institutional
  neurosis sufferers, 3, 47
Aid(s), therapeutic, in treatment of
  institutional neurosis, 27–44
— — alteration of attitude of
  professional staff, seen as, 49–57
Apathy, as sign of institutional
  neurosis, 2
Assessment of mental hospital, marking
  system for, 68
Atmosphere of ward (*see* Ward
  atmosphere)
Authority, charismatic, 56
— exercise of, in running a psychiatric
  service, 56–57
— sapiential, 56
— structural, 56

Bornholm's disease, 2
Bossiness of staff, arising from faulty
  administrative structures, 16
— — as factor in institutional neurosis,
  6, 15–16
— — group responsibility for, 16
Brutality, browbeating and teasing,
  eradication of, 44–57
— — — as factor in institutional
  neurosis, 6, 7, 10–15
— eradication of, specific measures to
  achieve, 46–48
— to be distinguished from necessary
  physical restraint, 47

Clothes, well-fitting, essential for
  patient's rehabilitation, 35–36
Consideration, clinical features and
  differential diagnosis of institutional
  neurosis, 1–5
— of the factors associated with
  institutional neurosis, 8–21
Contact with outside world, loss of, as
  factor in institutional neurosis, 6, 8–9
— — — — re-establishment of
  patient's, (*Figs.* 3, 4, 5) 27–44
Cooking and household management,
  revival of patient's skills in, 37

Depressive illnesses, differential
  diagnosis from institutional neurosis,
  4
Differential diagnosis of institutional
  neurosis, 4–5
Drugs, sedative, excessive use of, as
  factor in institutional neurosis,
  7, 18–19
— — reduction of, in treatment of
  institutional neurosis, 61–63

Electric convulsive therapy, 18, 54

Factors associated with institutional
  neurosis (*see also* under individual
  headings), 6–7
Friends, encouragement for patients to
  have, 57–58, 72
— League of, (*Figs.* 1, 2, 3) 30, 32, 37,
  58, 59, 61, 69–70, 72
— outside hospital, making patient
  aware of prospects of, 72–73
— personal, loss of, as factor in
  institutional neurosis, 6, 16–17

Government reports (*see* Inquiries)
Grooming, toilet and self-care,
  patient's, 35–36

Haematoma auris, 12–13
Harshness, as factor in institutional
  neurosis, 13–14

Hospital administrators and professional staff, relations between, 55
— programmes (*see* Programmes)

Idleness, enforced, as factor in institutional neurosis, 6, 9–10
Individuality, loss of, as sign of institutional neurosis, 2
Initiative, lack of, as sign of institutional neurosis, 2
Inquiries, governmental, into alleged ill-treatment of patients, 11–12
Institutional neurosis, consideration, clinical features and differential diagnosis of, 1–5
— — summary of, 76–77
— — synonyms for, 1
— — treatment of, 22–73
— — wider implications of, 74–75
Interest, loss of, as sign of institutional neurosis, 2

Loneliness of discharged patient, means of combating, 72–73
— patient's fear of suffering, in outside world, 21

Medical and nursing staff, alteration of attitude of, 49–57
Mental Health Services, History of the (Jones), 11
Myxoedema, differential diagnosis from institutional neurosis, 4

Noise in wards, 66–67
Nursing staff, alteration of the attitude of medical and, 49–57

'Oblomovism', 2
Occupations, provision of, for patients, (*Fig.* 4) 32–34
Organic dementias, differential diagnosis from institutional neurosis, 4
Outside world, loss of contact with (*see* Contact)

Patient's notes, providing evidence of institutional neurosis, 3–4
Personal events, encouragement for patient to enjoy, 61
— — loss of, as factor in institutional neurosis, 6, 17–18
— friends (*see* Friends)

Personal habits, deterioration in, as sign of institutional neurosis, 2
— possessions, encouraging patient to have, 58–59
— — loss of, as factor in institutional neurosis, 6, 17
— — provision of bedside furniture for patient's, (*Fig.* 6) 58–60
Physical exercise in rehabilitation of patients, 38–39
Posture characteristic of institutional neurosis, (*Frontispiece*) 3
Primary therapist, 28, 32, 33, 36
Professional staff, alteration of attitude of, as measure in treating institutional neurosis, 49–57
— — and hospital administrators, relations between, 55
Programme(s) card, patient's personal, (*Fig.* 4) 32–33, 34
— distinction between patient's, ward, and hospital, 42
— hospital, (*Fig.* 5) 41–44
— patient's, 32–33
— ward, 34–41
Prospects outside institution, loss of, as factor in institutional neurosis, 7, 20–21
Psychotherapy, individual, ill-effects of excessive consumption of doctor's time in, 54

Recreation(s), in rehabilitation of patients, (*Fig.* 4) 32–35, 37–38
— work seen as, 70–72
Religious belief of patients, not to be belittled, 42
Role in life, loss of, on entering institution, 21

Sans Everything (Robb), 11, 12
Schizophrenia, differential diagnosis from institutional neurosis, 4
Self-care, patient's (*see* Grooming)
Sheltered workshops, 40, 41
Social events for patients, provision of, (*Figs.* 4, 5) 32–44
— skills and poise, revival of patient's, 36–37
— services, public, role of, in obviating need for admissions to institutions, 26
Staff, bossiness of (*see* Bossiness)
— professional (*see* Professional staff)

Staff, senior, support by, essential for achievement of changes in institution, 27

Submissiveness, as sign of institutional neurosis, 2

Teasing, eradication of, 44–57
— as factor in institutional neurosis, 14–15
Therapy (*see also* Aids)
— electric convulsive, 18, 54
— by encouragement for patients to have friends, possessions, social events, 57–61
— provision of homely ward atmosphere, 63–68
Treatment of institutional neurosis, 22–73
— — — cross-reference chart as guide to, (*Fig.* 2) 24–25, 26
— — — ladder chart of stages in, (*Fig.* 1) 22–23
— — — objectives, considered in association with aetiological factors, 24–26
— — — summary of, 77

Visitors, importance of encouraging, 30
— — good facilities for, 8–9

Ward atmosphere, 19
— — depressing, as factor in institutional neurosis, 7, 19
— — homely, friendly and permissive, as measure in treatment of institutional neurosis, 63–68
White Rabbit, The (Marshall), 17
Work, loss of confidence in ability to, 21
— outside hospital, making patient aware of prospects of, 70–72
— — — re-establishment of patient's work pattern prior to, 70–72
— provision of, in rehabilitation of patient, 39–41
— seen as recreation, 70–72